ACKNOWLEDGMENTS

First, I want to thank God for blessing me to become the Man I am today. Without his Grace and Mercy, I would have been gone, like the ones I used to hang out with. God, your blessings have allowed me to hold a photographic memory in my head, of scenes with "relations" and people I have associated myself with. Over my years of growing, I acknowledge the way you have helped me to grow in patience and understanding. Thank You God for the dedication and persistence you instilled in me to start and finish this book. Thank you also for blessing me with a spiritual mother, who introduced me to you through her faithfulness. To my father Jessie Jones, Rest in Heaven Dad, A man I will always respect and love for never breaking bad on his family, even when the struggle was tough! To all of my siblings, thank you for wrapping your arms around me when it was really cold. Again God, I thank you for all my kids, from the oldest to the youngest. To all my babies, thank you for helping me be a great father. To all the real characters in this book, Thank you. Without you Angels, this book wouldn't exist. To the best chapter in my life today, My Family. The ones that are still giving me that unconditional love and support, Thank You. To all my readers that know me or don't know me, I want to thank you also for taking this valuable time out of your life, to read my book. I hope that it gives you the pleasurable entertainment just as well as some education. I want everyone to know, that I truly appreciate your love. GAMETIME… NO TIME FOR PRACTICE!

INSIDE of THE GAME

By: Mac Goldie

Chapter 1

It was in the month of July on a hot hellish evening, when I was dressed in my sky blue Coogi short set, with my white cloud gator sandals. Sitting behind the wheels of a Black blue Sedan Cadillac Deville, listening to Curtis Mayfield sing, "The Life We Live is Beautiful." Smoking on some fire weed that the city of Memphis call, "Chicken." They call it chicken because of the way it made you choke and jerk your neck like a rooster.

Not only did I have on the colors that match the sky, but I also felt like I was floating on clouds of ecstasy.

Because of the blazing heat on the outside, I was forced to adjust my A.C to blow snowballs out of the vents on the inside. I also adjusted my rear-view mirror, so that I could see that beautiful hoe nature called sunshine peeping from behind the clouds. Yes! It was a wonderful day for the Pimps, hoes and tricks to sweat the track. Either looking for business or pleasure for a respectable fee.

I was one of the few Pimps that would put their hoes down on the concrete, whether it was hot, cold, raining or snowing. This was my way of seeing whether or not my hoes had any dedication for my Pimping. I didn't believe in putting my hoes in any strip clubs, escort service or massage parlor. To me, that's what makes a hoe lazy and considered by full bloody Pimps, half of a HOE. I felt like the concrete was for true Pimps and Hoes. Plus, I liked to Pimp for my money by giving my hoes the game to sell in the streets.

Me and another pimp name Goldy Locs passed one another riding down Steward Ave, giving a special way Pimps blow their horns. Goldie Locs knew I wanted to kick some pimping, so he made an illegal U-turn in the middle of the streets making traffic come to a complete stop, as if his Pimping was a red light. I loved Goldy Locs. He was an immaculate dresser and a drug free Pimp, that Pimped strictly by the book of his laws. He didn't allow his hoes to smoke, drink or use anything that would interfere with his Pimping. Because of the way he Pimped, was one of the reasons he couldn't keep a hoe for over a week. But this still didn't change his laws in Pimping.

I met Goldy Locs through a blind hoe of his that had mistaken me as being him. Goldy Locs and I had similar features such as our height, our way of dressing and our quality smile. He was more beautiful than the sun coming up and the moon going down with all of his teeth cover with gold and diamonds. I was more beautiful than the ass on a peacock, with a smile that made a hoe freeze from my bottom grill. I call every gold tooth in my mouth trophies for how many hoes I done broke, and every diamond on my teeth was for the hoes I turned into stars.

Chapter 2

One night on Pimp hours, I was cruising down Peachtree doing 15mph looking and fishing for me a hoe that was in need of a Pimp. The streets were empty and there wasn't a hoe in sight. I thought to myself, maybe vice done had one of their major sweeps and arrested everything with long legs in a skirt.

I noticed in my rearview the police was trying to run my tag number by the way his car was flirting with my Pimp mobile. Turning my signal on to make a right on Spring Street, he finally decided to throw on his disco lights pulling me over.

I didn't panic. I was angrier than I was scared. I knew there was nothing he could do to me besides write me a ticket or interview my Pimping. When he approached the car, I was reaching into my wallet for my license. All four of my windows was tinted so that you couldn't see what was on the inside. I can tell he was a hater by the way his hee-haw accent blurted out, "Howdy, can I see your license, registration and insurance please?" Before showing him anything, I asked, "Is there a problem?" He said, "Yep, you made an improper turn back at the red light." Looking at him as if I was a black panther from the seventies as I took my time to show him my license. After taking over five minutes to run my information, he finally came back saying, "Sorry about the inconvenience, have a nice day."

I popped my collar and put my Pimping in gear as I decided to exercise my game in this titty Bar called *The Gentleman Club.* This is where I broke Goldy's ex-hoe name Co-Co for mistaking me as being him. As soon as I entered the club, every trick, baller and hoe was sweating my Pimping, as if I was a record producer looking for talent. I sat at the bar and ordered me a double shot of Hennessy with a glass of coke.

Some young Janet Jackson looking bitch came over asking could she have a dance. Without looking at her body, I looked into her eyes and said, "Listen Pretty, the only thing I'm gonna give you is some words of understanding." I can tell she was a renegade by the way she disrespected my Pimping, asking for money. Either that, or she was a square bitch fresh in the game. Before I could caress her mind with some understanding of who I am and what I do, some faggot bitch whispered in her ear, rolled her eyes at me, grabbed her hand and stole the bitch from my presence. Never once did I blow my cool or show any emotion toward the steal. I did feel uncomfortable in an unfamiliar environment that I wasn't used to knocking hoes from. As I said earlier, I was a concrete pimp who fish for street walkers, not hoes who entertain tricks by dancing.

Just when I was about to leave, all of a sudden, the game sent some little pretty hoe with a Good Times fro' and Colgate smile breathing like she just finished up with a trick.

"Hey Daddy!" She said excited. "I've been calling you all night, but your phone keeps going straight to your voicemail. Here's $375 and I have a trick right now that's going to give me a bill in the V.I.P room." Not really believing what this stupid bitch had done, I played crazy as she was and said, "Hurry up baby with that trick so we can get out of here."

"But Daddy it's only one o'clock and the club is flooded with tricks!"

"I know baby, but we really have something to talk about."

"Okay Daddy," she answered back leery.

No later than twenty minutes she was dress to meet the right game but the wrong man she had given her money to. Never once did Co-Co look me in my face, until we got outside, and she still didn't notice the mistake she made. Before we got into my car, I grabbed her by her hands and looked her directly in her eyes and said, "What's your name Lil' Pretty?"

She laughed and said, "Stop playing Daddy!"

"No bitch! Straight up. What's your name?" She started noticing the talk and change of attitude I was showing her and suddenly her vision was clear and aware of what she had done. She dropped her head as if she was trying to show respect for Goldy Locs now. But it was too late for her to get in order after what she has already done.

I gently manipulated her into getting inside my car so we can get a better understanding. She was froze and spooked as she held her purse and dance bag close to her. "Listen Lil' Pretty, you might think this was a mistake, but it really wasn't. Everything happens for a reason. I usually don't go inside titty bars, but tonight, I felt some hoe with boss potential needed a true pimp to bring it out of her." She remained froze as I continued to Mack for that hundred-dollar bill she had from the V.I.P.

You know it's cool to rundown to me about you and your ex-man. She felt comfortable when I asked her to run down Goldy Locs to me. She raised her head up as if some weight had been taken off her and said, "What's your name?"

"I'm Mac Goldie baby, better known as The Game."

She said, "Well my name is Stacy, but everyone calls me Co-Co."

I flirted and said, "I see why. Where you from Co-Co?"

"New York," she said in a proper accent. "Do you wear glasses or contact lens?"

"Yes! Contact lens why?"

"Yes, why? Because maybe you should trade them in for some better ones, so you won't make this same mistake again."

She smiled as if she was advertising a Colgate toothpaste commercial. I continued to say, "You do know what you have done right?"

"Yes," she mumbled. Are you going to tell Goldy about this stupid mistake I made?"
"Yes I am. But the choice you made wasn't a mistake or stupid. You made the right move and wise choice to give your money to someone who's going to bring the best out of you. Put more time into you, so that you will know the difference between me and an identical twin who claim to look like me."
"What if I don't want to leave Goldy?"
"You already left him pretty baby when you put this money in my hand. Now show me this wasn't no mistake and break yourself for everything you have in that dance bag and purse." I continued macking telling her, "You'll be safe with me, as long as I know you're my woman. But you going to have to show me that you are for my Pimping just as much as I am for your hoeing. And the way to do that baby is put all your trust into me."
She mumbled, "I'm scared Goldie." I said, "That's cause you still believing in yourself baby. Now show me your belief

is in Mac Goldie the Game and break yourself to a new beginning of us."

She reached in her purse and gave me a hundred and fifty more dollars along with Goldy Locs number to call. I ran down to her that loyalty and respect means more to me than any dollar bill you give me.

"So, I'm going to ask you before I tell you to strip naked, do you have any more money or any values to give me?"

She shouted, "What do you mean? Don't you trust your hoes?"

"Yes, I do, but only when I know I'm inside your head and walking through your legs. And right now, you and I haven't built these feelings."

She thought by her shedding tears she could con me into believing she didn't have any more money. But by me being hip to the secret spot hoes hide their money, I wanted to see not hear my answer. She stripped naked and spread her low mileage pussy as open as she could. When I seen how little her pussy was, I said to myself, *Christ! I wondered if she's a baby!* That's when I asked to see some identification. She said everything is in my purse. I shook down her purse hoping she was old enough to pay my Pimping. When I seen the age on her State Identification, I was relieved. I still had to skull her to see does her ways match the I.D.

She was a great actress because every skull game I ran on her matched the age on the I.D. Now it was time to lace her up with my rules and regulations. Before I could embrace her with my first law, she reached inside her purse for her phone that was constantly going off and said excited, "Daddy! This is a trick that comes in the club and gives me $250. He's in there right now! Please, let me go break him so I could give you some more money!" I was excited just as much as she was about giving me more money.

She con me into believing she was going right in and back out no later than 30 minutes. Like a sucker with a blow pop

15

wrapped around my face I said, "Okay hurry back."

Soon as she went in the club, I went in ten minutes after her. I watched her with my own two eyes disappeared in my face. First, I wasn't sure was it her because of the disco lights flashing off and on. But after 30 mins went by, I knew she was the unsure hoe I seen leaving the club with a trick who looked like the Incredible Hulk, the bouncer.

I smiled and checked my Rolex watch to see what time it was. I had spent two hours with Co-Co for five hundred twenty-five dollars. As far as I was concerned, she paid for my time and the mistake she made. I still had her clothes, I.D, and Goldy Locs number. I wasn't sure if I should call Goldy and serve him the news because I didn't have his hoe. As far as I know, she probably beat me telling him the rundown but not the way it really happened. I wanted bad to meet Goldy Locs because I really wanted to see if him and I looked alike, so my hoes wouldn't make the same mistake his blind hoe made.

Chapter 3

I waited the next day to call Goldy Locs because I was too tired to meet him that night. He answered the phone on the first ring as if he was waiting up all night for my call.

"Hello," he said in a curious tone.

"What's happening Goldy Locs, this Mac Goldie, some more pimping."

"What's happening Mac Goldie, do I know you?"

"You may not know me but I'm sure you heard of me just like I heard of you." He said, "Oh yeah, my hoe told me early this morning she ran into somebody who popped on her like they was me and took her money." I laughed in an unbelievable tone and said, "Dig this Goldy Locs, I don't take money I mack for mines. Now that little lying hoe of yours was either blind, drunk, high or crazy when she mistaken me as being you and gave me your trap. I knew she wasn't aware of who I was, so I took her on the outside of the club so she can get a better look, and also so we could get a better understanding about what she had done. She still didn't know the difference, until I hipped her that I'm the right game but the wrong man you have given your money to. She acted as if she wanted to break her ankles and get away, but the surprising news had paralyzed her body from moving. Once, I gave her a better understanding about what she had done and what we could do about it to make it official. She got in my car and felt comfortable to share with me the rest of her money she made that night. Before I could lace her up with my rules, she played con on me as if some trick was in the club that will give her more money to give to me. I bought the lie and she never came back. But that's not the reason I'm calling you Goldy Locs, I'm calling so maybe later this evening, you and I can hook up and have lunch on what I broke that bitch for."

He said, "sure Mac Goldie. Meet me at the underground in front of five points at two o'clock pm."

"That's cool time," I said Goldy Locs, and I agreed to meet.

After I hung up the phone, standing in front of my bedroom door, was a tall six-foot beautiful blonde with a money trap in one hand and my breakfast in the other one.

"Good Morning Daddy, can I come in?"

"Sure, Pretty Angel, where are the rest of the girls?"

"Everyone is in the living room waiting on you to give us a rundown for today." Jazz was my bottom hoe and the one I could depend on through a storm.

"Here's my trap Daddy, its sixteen hundred and eighty dollars. I took twenty out to buy you breakfast. Daddy, I think Melissa wanted to talk to you about something, do you want me to tell her it's cool to come in?"

"Not now Jazz, roll me a blunt and run me some bath water, then take that breakfast you got for me and give it to Foxy. Make sure once she finishes eating to put her ass back outside, cause you know how she's quick to take a shit on my mink carpet."

Foxy was the first dog I copped for a friend. She was a red nose Pit with a heart like mines.

After Jazz left the room my youngest hoe Infinity came in behind her. Infinity was a good actress and a great thief. She also was possessive and a future downfall in my game.

"Hey Daddy, I'm not feeling good."

"What's wrong baby daughter," I asked with counterfeit concern. Because I knew she was faking and wanted some attention.

"I don't know Daddy; my head is hurting, and my stomach is cramping."

"I know why your head is hurting hoe, cause you trying to do my job which is too much thinking! Now kiss my fist and gain some strength so you can steal Daddy a bankroll to pay for my new 2001 Cadillac Escalade Truck next year." She smiled as if what I had said took all her pain away. Then said, "Daddy please let me be the one who buy your next Caddy!"

"You will be baby fox, now go outside and test the weather so Daddy can know what suit I'm going to wear today." She came back less than one minute with that beautiful smile and said, "Daddy it feels good today!" So, since the weather was right and my game was tight, I told Infinity to take my butterfly Coogi suit out the closet and my Hoe catching Pimp scent.

When I was in the tub, I was thinking about what Goldy Locs stupid hoe told him. Laughing out loud, my thickest hoe Michelle heard me and knocked on the door asking, "Are you okay Daddy?"

Michelle was a pretty hoe with some thick ass thighs, she had titties like apples with some money green eyes. I knocked her in Daytona Beach, FL. She was a square bitch and a neighborhood slut to her community. I came into her life and introduced her to the game of pimping and hoeing. She was fascinated by the game and fame and chose my Pimping with a square paycheck that added up to a choosing fee. The same night she chose my Pimping I worked her for over sixteen hours to see if she was qualified to hoe for me. That morning she brought in her qualification by giving me a twenty-two-hundred-dollar trap. She was so motivated until she couldn't wait to go back to work. Yes, my Pimping was definitely in the moves she was making!

Michelle asked, "Daddy, is it cool for me to come in?"

"Yes, baby girl, come on in." I can tell that she wanted to see a Pimp naked because out of the six month she been with me she never got the chance to see or feel my Pimp sex affection. Already covered up in my hundred-dollar bill towel, Michelle might have to wait another month before she get the chance to witness my nudeness.

Smiling like the first day she gave me twenty-two hundred she said, "Daddy, can I work off Shallow Ford Road today?"
"What's wrong with where you working now," I asked?
"The police over there knows me and told me, if he sees me again over there I'm going to jail."
"Are you afraid to go to jail, or you don't think Daddy is going to bail you out?" She acted as if I hurt her feelings because I felt like she didn't believe in me and said,
"Daddy, you know all my belief is in you and I would never doubt your integrity! I just don't want to get arrested and cost you any money."
"Don't worry about getting arrested, take my instructions with you to work and I promise you will make it back to me successful and safe."
"Yes Daddy," she said with a believable smile. Before she left out, I told her to tell Melissa to wait on me inside her room. I sent all the girls except Melissa to cop them some breakfast. Waiting patiently in

her room like I instructed her to she looked like a high school graduate waiting on her date to take her to the prom.

Melissa was beautiful! Her complexion was pecan with a little peanut butter mix in with it. She also was a great thief. I believed she stole her beautiful tan from the TV Show, *Bay Watch.* Melissa was from Kansas City, but I stole her from a car dealer con man in Memphis, Tennessee. She was playing secretary when me and my bottom hoe Jazz walked in looking for Jazz a car. I can tell she was going to be my third hoe the way she leaped to her feet with enthusiasm to help Jazz and me. Although I was enthused as much as she was, I stayed cool and played her right into my Pimp trap.

"Can I help you?" she asked.

"You sure can," I said. "First, I must ask, do you know anything about cars?"

"A little," she answered. "What type of car are you looking for?"

"Well, to be honest, I'm really looking for a nice car for my Angel right here."

Before, she could say anything, I cut her off saying, "Now this is an angel that fell from the sky, took my game to hell and trick the devil for his fire. This is also a hoe that have made me millions by dating tricks, selling lies and stealing me jewelry…. she has put miles on her feet through Arizona heat, blister on her toes in the snow and cold, now tell me Melissa, which one of these cars you think deserves to have my hoe?" She was froze with nothing to say, so I left her with Jazz to answer all the questions she wanted to know about me. I spoke with the manager to see how much he wanted for this 1997 STS Cadillac Deville that I had eyes on for Jazz. I wasn't going to get it yet until I came up with Melissa to make her pay for it.

Her and Jazz was having a good time discussing me, so later that night, Melissa had chosen up with six hundred dollars and a title to a 1996 Honda Accord that the car dealer gave her to work for him.

When I went in the room Melissa had her head down as if something heavy was on her mind.

"What's wrong baby star?" She broke down in tears telling me how her kids father was trying to take the kids from her because of the lifestyle she was living. I place her damp face on my chest and said, "stop crying about something that's not going to happen. Next week you and I are going to straighten all of your legal business."

"FOREAL Daddy!" She said in an unbelievable tone.

"Hoe have I ever lied to you about anything?"

"No Daddy," she said, and hug me as if she had already won her kids back and said, "I love you Daddy."

"It's cool to love me baby but fall in love with my Pimping!"

"Yes Daddy."

By the time Melissa and I finished from talking, the girls had made it back and it was time to get the game started for the day. Everybody was dress to catch and feeling like the first day of spring.

Chapter 4

I was Pimping in a brand new, 1999 Sedan Deville that my bottom hoe Jazz gave birth to on March 4, 1999. My youngest hoe Infinity was already 3 months pregnant by my Pimping and was due to give birth to a brand new 2000 Cadillac Escalade.

Every hoe who stayed down for my pimping over a year, I have pimped either an automobile or an immaculate crib out of her cunt. The first hoe I dropped off was Michelle. As soon as she got out the car, a red light full of tricks was waiting on her. Michelle was a pimps dream and a trick fiend. She was a traffic stopper even when the light was green.

The next hoe was Melissa. She was so beautiful she had to sneak on the track. I hated to see her go but I loved to watch her leave.

My third stop hoe was Infinity. She will always take a blow pop with her to work. When she sucked on that blow pop, she can make a Priest committee a sin. Her favorite line to the tricks was, "Hi, I just turned 18 will you fuck me in my ass?" The tricks couldn't resist that round ass of hers.

Jazz was the last hoe I would drop off every day. She could hit the track late and still out do every hoe in my stable. I called her my **MVP**, *Most Valuable Prostitute.* She stood over six feet in some heels and had some ocean blue eyes, the color of the sky. You would have thought she played on The Young and Restless instead of the track flipping tricks. YES, Jazz was a for sure thousand dollars every night!

After I had all of my hoes down, it was close to two o'clock pm. I just remember Goldy Locs, and I was supposed to meet up at two o'clock. I was 45 minutes from where we was supposed to meet at, so I decided to give him a call to see what area he was in.

"Was happening, Mac Goldie where you at?"

"I'm 45 minutes from downtown, what about you?"

"I'm already downtown posted, trying to catch me a hoe!"

"Dig that baby, dig that," I said. "Well give me 30 minutes and I should be pulling in on the set."

"See you when you get here," he said.

Twenty minutes later, I was downtown on Peachtree. Five minutes from five points, I spotted Goldy a mile away looking like a tropical fruit. Dressed in a yellow Versace shirt, some orange linen pants, yellow gator shoes and an orange Godfather hat on his head that represented who he was, which was a Pimp! I noticed the resemblance of Goldy and I. He definitely was a reflection of me! Looking for a spot to park my pimping I reached inside my compartment and grabbed my V.I.P parking sticker, which was a handicap pass I bought from an old woman.

Goldy Locs acted as if he smelled my pimping before he saw me by the way he paralyzed his eyes on my presence. We greeted one another with honor and pleasure. Not believing how much we looked alike Goldy said, "CHRIST!" I finally met my twin!"

He introduced me to this guy I thought was a Pimp but was a con man. Really, he had game in all four of his pockets. In one pocket he was screaming Pimping, in the next pocket he was selling slum jewelry, in his back pocket he had counterfeit money and in the last pocket was the most world-famous hustle, "The three-card motley." His name was Slick Frank, and he had more game than the show The Price Is Right, but he was far from being Bob Barker, because he didn't believe in making no deals. It was either his way or no way when it came down to the business.

Slick Frank was close to seventy years old but still had dreams like a kid in the ghetto. Frank, Goldy and I was posted in front of The Underground Mall, when some beautiful looking bitch stepped up to Slick Frank asking to buy some jewelry. Respecting the code in the game, Goldy and I didn't interfere into the fast sweet lick Frank was about to break the innocent bitch for. You can tell she was a square and a green bean, the way she pulled a choosing fee trap out of her purse in front of three smooth talking players, who sell game for a living. Not believing his eyes or the scenery, Slick Frank quickly grabbed her by the hands and walked away with her. "Make sure you lace that green bitch Frank," is what Godly Locs screamed out!

After standing in front of the Underground Mall for over an hour, I asked Goldy did he want to bend some blocks and shake down the corner looking for hoes. He said shamefully, "Mac Goldie, I don't have any wheels mane! That hoe that you broke last night, was going to be my next ride, but she blowed before I could Pimp it out of her.

She was two weeks old in my life before she broke bad, and I was only breaking her for show money not hoe money." He continued to say, "Goldie mane I been down on my luck for some months now, but nothing has knocked my belief. Just because I don't have a hoe right now doesn't mean I'm not a Pimp!"

Goldy Locs didn't know that his Pimp devotion had captivated my Pimp emotion for him. Instantly, I fell in love with his Pimping! Not only did he have a real friend for a Pimp, but I was devoted to being his strength, motivation and Pimp support until he caught him a hoe.

Goldy and I rode around the whole city of Atlanta macking and Pimping, building a durational relationship. The moves and the way we put our game down is how we knew it was Pimping with the both of us. I was hipping Godly Locs on to the sweet spots I be fishing for me a hoe, before I was interrupted by a phone call from my thief hoe Infinity. She was breathing hard and talking faster than Elmer Fudge the cartoon character. I knew that she had stolen a wallet with them extra finger she uses to pick pocket tricks with.

"Daddy, Daddy will you please come pick me up from the McDonalds on Buford Highway? I'm hiding in the rest room from this Mexican, I just took forty-two hundred dollars from!" I said in a nonchalant voice, "Hoe, which McDonald's you at?"

"The one by Doraville precinct," she said nervously.

"Be still hoe, and make sure you get away with my money!"

Goldy Locs heard everything! He was just excited as I was about the lick, but both of us kept our emotions in the freezer as if the lick meant nothing to us. We were Pimps! Not Suckers! And we didn't believe nothing a hoe said until she put it in a Pimp's hand. But on the inside, I was motivated as a young Pimp who just broke his first hoe! Within 20 minutes I was on Buford Highway, three mins from the McDonald's Infinity called me from.

Infinity came running out bare footed with her heels in her hands. When she jumped in the back seat, she noticed some more Pimping was in the car. She immediately froze her hoeing and dropped her head towards the floor. This was nothing strange to Goldy Locs. He was hipped to the rules a Pimp laced his hoe with when she's in the presence of another Pimp.

Riding to the nearest expressway, I cracked the back windows so Infinity could listen to nature instead of me and Goldie's conversation. Listening to Curtis Mayfield sing "Do Be You and Do be Down, I asked Goldy was he cool with riding with me to Pensacola, FL so he can come up on a hoe. He answered, "Does a bear shit in the woods!!!! You damn right I will ride with you!! I'm ready to blow this town." He shamefully lowered the tone in his voice and said, "But first Goldie I have to come up with my rent money before I leave." I said, "Don't sweat it Pimping, we going to squash that before we hit the road." Goldy looked at me as if he wanted to hug me but instead, he reached his hand out and said, "I'll never forget you Mac Goldie, and you can believe that!"

Chapter 5

By this time, we was close to Greyhound bus station where I told Infinity to go inside and wait for me to come in. Giving me an eye to eye contact she bobbed her head toward the back arm rest letting me know that's where she put the forty-two hundred dollars. I peeped the signal and told her with my eyes to go inside. From the minute she got out the car she paralyzed the whole parking lot with them long milky way chocolate legs. Even Goldy Locs took a peep at her commercial curves and said, "Damn Mac Goldie you're Pimping sure do make that fine hoe of yours beautiful." I agreed with him and said, "Yea mane it took some time to turn that tramp to a champ, and she still have a lot of growing to do."

We both stepped out the car looking like Hollywood and Las Vegas. Goldy Locs played the outside while I went on the inside to rap with Infinity about the money she stole. Sitting all the way in the back of the bus station I can feel Infinity eyes staring through my pants, with a look on her face as if something was going to happen tonight.

Before I could make it to the table she quickly jumped up and pulled my chair out so I could sit down. I taught all of my girls mannerism when it comes to serving a Pimp. They knew it wasn't a dollar they could give me without the respect and loyalty first. I believed in pimping these standards and expectation in my hoes so that my money wouldn't be funny when I checked it. Infinity was sipping on a strong soda when I asked her about the lick earlier. The reason I say that is because after taking a good swallow of her Coca-Cola, she gasped for some breath. Then she said, "Daddy that lick for that $4,200 was sweet!! I caught this Mexican drunk with his wallet laying on the dresser. By the time I crept the wallet, his friend peeped me trying to stuff it in my pussy. His friend said something in Spanish, which made his friend start looking for his wallet. I couldn't understand nothing in Spanish they was saying but the body language was speaking good English which meant "GET THE FUCK OUT OF THERE!!!! He tried reaching his hand out to grab me, but I sprayed him with my mace, and put my hoeing in drive. Daddy I wasn't scared of the Mexican, I was more worried about getting away with your money. Daddy, I believe the game knew how bad I wanted this lick." Still not showing any emotions from the lick I said, "Baby Thief, I'm not surprise about the lick you just made. This is how the game will reward you when you take my Pimping to work with you. It's going to be bigger licks than this for you in the game baby. That's why you have to stay ten toes down for my Pimping, okay baby?"

"Okay Daddy, she smiled then kiss my fist.

"Infinity, I have a new spot that I want you to work for the rest of the night. There's going to be some out-of-pocket hoes out there that need some game so make sure you keep your eyes open for me a steal." She asked curiously, "Daddy, what do you mean a steal? For a lick or another hoe?"

"Bitch don't ever try and give me a choice!! I mean the lick and the next bitch!"

Chapter 6

It was close to six o'clock and time for the other girls to call and give me a rundown on the streets. The first call that I received was from my pretty little bitch Melissa.

"Hey Daddy!"

I answered, "What's going on sunshine?"

"Why do you always call me sunshine?"

Without hesitating I said, "Because Pretty every time my days be partly cloudy with a 90% chance of rain, soon as I hear from you the sun starts back to shine in my life."

I can feel her blushing thought the phone before saying, "Daddy I only have $760 and a trick that's going for the $150 right now."

I said, "Well baby don't let me hold the game up get back to work."

As soon as I was hanging up from her, Michelle was on the other end with a story without the glory. She said in demotivated voice, "Hi Daddy." Before I could say anything, she kept talking.

"Daddy I only have $460 since I've been out here. It's hot Daddy and plus the same police officer I was telling you about threatened to take me to jail if he sees me again."

I said, "Listen Baby Star and listen good! The next time that freak police choose you to harass make sure to tell him you have a job to do just like he do. Tell him he either can give you some money or take you to jail. Now, how much money you said you done already made?"

She mumbled, "$460."

"Okay Michelle, if it's that hot outside, take a couple of dollars out my money, buy you a soda and keep hoeing." Before she can say anything, I had already hung up the phone. One thing I didn't believe in when it came down to my Pimping was excuses. I would always tell my hoes to sell them tricks the story and bring me back the glory.

Goldy Locs was listening to the way I was Pimping, and he said in a motivating Pimp spirit, "PIMP OR DIE BABY!!!!" I popped my collar and said, "I'm going to keep Pimping mane!" In the middle of our conversation, I received another phone call, this time from my bottom hoe Jazz. Already knowing her trap was right I didn't answer, instead I let the voicemail catch her. She left a message saying, "Daddy, this Jazz, I'm ahead of the game and my score is $870. I wanted to ask you if it's okay I catch a cab back to the room and change clothes? I got into a fight with this Mexican and he ripped the buttons off my shirt. Please call me as soon as you get this message!" Before I could call her back, she was calling again.

"Hello?" I said in a concerned tone!

"Hi Daddy, did you get my message?"

"Yes, I did, and I want to know why you fighting with this Mexican when you supposed to be breaking on him?"

"No Daddy, can I explain? The Mexican was taking too long to cum so I told him to give me more money for more time. He tried to hold me down and muscle me, so when I pushed him off me, he grabbed my shirt and ripped my blouse."

"Are you ok?" I asked out of Pimp concern.

"YES," I just need to change clothes and get back to work."

"Where are you now Jazz?"

"Inside Denny's waiting on a taxi."

"Okay cool, when you make it to your room put my money under the mattress and your code in my pager letting me know that you made it there safe and back to work."

"Yes Daddy," she answered in a relieved voice.

By this time, we was riding down Memorial Drive, close to Stone Mountain in DeKalb County, where I was getting ready to put Infinity down for the night. Riding through some apartment called, *The Colony,* I was giving her a rundown on what areas to work and what kind of tricks to do business with. This was a community full of young black drug dealers, girls that was renegades and plenty of Mexicans who couldn't wait to see a hoe working.

Once I let Infinity out at the back of the apartments, she was placed back on the clock getting my money. As I said earlier, Infinity was a lucky hoe that had skills when it came down to my Pimping.

Before Goldy Locs and I could get back on the expressway she was calling to let me know just that quick she had stolen $400.

I said, "Damn Hoe is the money hot?"

"No Daddy, as soon as you let me out, I walked into this Mexican house and four-hundred-dollar bills was just sitting there on top of the TV. Nobody was there in the house. Daddy I crept in and out of the apartment without anyone noticing me."

I said, "Damn baby angel you are an incredible Hoe, but if you call me back within ten minutes, talking about you done took some more money, you going to make me feel like you done already

stole a million dollars and only giving me a portion of it instead of it all!!"
She said in disbelief, "Daddy I can't believe you said that!!! I never hold or fold any money from you!!! My loyalty is in every move I make for you."
I said in a cold bloody tone, "Well bitch make some more moves, then I hung up the phone.

Goldy Locs had the remote to the radio and press mute then said, "Mac Goldie Mane I sure love the way you Pimp!!!"
It was twenty minutes after eight when we pulled up at Goldy Locs apartment. He lived on Fulton Industrial, which was known for robbers, drug dealers and junkies. I was concerned for Goldy when I asked him, "How long you been living here Pimping?"
He said with a secured look on his face, "For eight months. Everyone knows me over here and they respect my Pimping too!!"

He invited me up to his room so that I would know what room he stayed in.

Feeling a little uncomfortable, I was moving really slow as if my legs had arthritis. I only knew Goldy Locs for eight hours and I knew he was hipped to all the money I checked off Infinity. But it was something about Goldy that made me feel comfortable once I stepped inside his room. This was not an average hotel room. Goldy Locs had his own carpet to match his king size waterbed and walls. In his closet was every color in the crayon box that matched his style and personality. I thought to myself, Yes, this is definitely a Pimp!!! and I felt safer in the presence of his company.

Goldy Locs offered me something to drink then begin showing me pictures of his Wall of Fame. Every picture came with a rundown about his ex-hoes and Pimping. I felt honored to know the history on his Pimping. He was popping on how six months ago he had six hoes and a brand-new Sedan Deville Cadillac with a future living.

When his bottom hoe left everyone took off behind her. He said, "Mac Goldie I been down on my luck for quite a minute now." I asked him out of Pimp concern, "How much is your rent Pimping?" "Mac Goldie I'm really too embarrassed to say, but I pay by the week and I'm already two weeks behind. I owe them $375." I reached in my pocket and gave Goldy Locs $600. He said looking surprise, "Mac Goldie I said $375 not $600!!!!" I said, "Well take the rest and buy yourself some dinner and a good breakfast in the morning and be ready to go cross country Pimping with me." Goldy Locs embraced me with an appreciation hug then said, "Mac Goldie you're more than a Pimp. Mane you are an angel that fell from the sky into my life. Allow me to walk you back to your car Goldie."

Outside of the room was a bad, pretty Indian looking fox stopped Goldy Locs and asked us was we twins?
"Yes, we are, come over and meet some more Pimping." She just smiled and kept

walking. I shook Goldy Locs hand and said, "Goldy it was a pleasure and honor to Pimp with you today. See you in the morning no later than twelve o'clock." Before I jumped back in traffic, I rolled me a blunt. I remember Goldy telling me he doesn't smoke or do any drugs, so I respected him by not smoking in his presence. The only drug I did was weed. I would take me a drink on certain occasions, but I smoked weed just like cigarettes. I had spent over two hours in Goldy Locs room macking, now it was close to eleven o'clock when I received a phone call from no Pimping Tennessee.

Tennessee wasn't a true Pimp to me, or other Pimps in the game because he would make moves on his own when his hoe had a bad night or didn't want to work. They both was looking for love in the wrong game. Tennessee was calling to be in my business like he always is, "What's up Mac Goldie the Game?" "What's happening Tennessee?" I said in a demotivating spirit. Still continue to talk saying, "I heard you copped a pretty little bitch last night from The Gentlemen's Club?"

I said, "Damn Tennessee, the only way you could have heard that was to be there."

He laughed back saying, "I guess you can say I was there. My girl worked last night, that's who told me saw you macking on the pretty bitch."

I roared through the phone saying, "Damn Tennessee, maybe I should've been in there checking your girlfriend trap since she had her eyes on my Pimping!!!"

He laughed in a fake tone saying, "You know my hoe don't know nobody but me and my Pimping, so Goldie don't go trying to count something that's not yours."

"What you say Nigga?" I said hoping he say it again so I can hang up on his three-dollar bill ass. Instead, I said, "Tennessee you should've been a News Reporter instead of half of a Pimp, maybe people will respect you more." Before he could say anything, I cut him off saying, "Let me call you back Tennessee, I have a phone call on the other end." On the other end of the phone was my bottom hoe Jazz. It was eleven o'clock and time for all my hoes to check in with a rundown.

"Hello.... Hello," Jazz said twice as if she didn't hear me say hello the first time. "Hi Daddy."

"What's up deaf hoe," I said for acting like she didn't hear me.

"Daddy, I'm not deaf, It's something wrong with this raggedy ass phone!" Cutting her off I said, "What's your score hoe?"

She answered back with respect saying, "Six hundred and forty dollars. Daddy the track has lost weight out here, there's no traffic or anymore hoes out here working. What do you want me to do?"

I said, "Go inside Denny's Jazz and wait for me, if any action come through there before I come, take care of it."

"Can I buy something to eat Daddy?" Jazz asked.

"Sure, Baby Angel, also order me some of them chicken strips with a strawberry cake."

"Okay Daddy," she said and hung up the phone.

Chapter 7

On my way to Jazz, I was close to where Michelle was, so I broke down my speed to give her time to call. Just like a candidate on time for her first interview, Michelle called me on time. Sounding like she had just finish from having an orgasm she said in a sexy voice, "Hi Daddy."
I said back in an icy tone, "What's up with you bitch! Did you and your favorite police officer ever get an understanding?" Laughing through the phone she said, "I sure did Daddy. After he saw I wasn't going to leave the track, he drove by smiling saying, "you're not going to learn until something bad happens to you huh?" I flirted back and said, "That's why I have you here to protect me my hero. Daddy he just smiled and said, "Be Careful."

"Where are you now Michelle?" I said sounding not interested in her freaky rundown!!!

"I'm in front of the Waffle House Daddy, on Shallow Ford Road. Do you want me to take a taxi back home?"

"NO!" Before she could say anything else, I was pulling up where she was.

When Michelle got into the car she slid all the way to the left, which was the spot she was in my stable. Reaching over my shoulder, she placed a nine-hundred-and-sixty-dollar trap in my hand then asked could she kiss my fist? Cold as the weather is in Alaska I said, "Not now baby, Later." Not knowing if I was mad at her about something, she just sat back and gave me a counterfeit smile through my rearview mirror.

The next call was from Tennessee again asking me, "Goldie, You still on the phone Pimping?"

Still not wanting to talk to him I said, "Yeah Tennessee, I'm still in the middle of the game." Any other Pimp wouldn't have lied, But as I said earlier, Tennessee was no Pimp. Therefore, I had no conscience for lying to him. Looking at my hoe bobbing her head to the music Rick James was macking on this song called, *Player's Way.* I can see my Pimping running all through her body.

Finally, Infinity and Melissa was calling at the same time. I say the same time because as soon as I was saying hello to Melissa, Infinity was ringing on the other end. Telling Melissa to pause for a minute I clicked over to Infinity and said, "What's the score Li Baby?"
"Daddy, I only have three hundred more dollars, including the four I took earlier. These are some cheap ass Mexicans, and they hard to steal from Daddy. Will you come put me down somewhere else so I can get you some more money?"
I said, "NO baby thief, I'm tied up right now.
Have one of them Mexican's take you to Jazz room and wait on me in the lobby."

"Yes Daddy," she said as I clicked over back to Melissa.

She said patiently, "Hi Daddy, I have $1285. Daddy I had $1300 but I had to spend ten dollars on a taxi and six on some more condoms. Daddy, my pussy is so sore I can barely walk!!!" She continued to say, "Daddy, will you please teach me to be a better thief because I'm tired of flipping all of these Mexicans?"

"Bitch, do you realize what you just said to me!!!"

"No Daddy, did I say something wrong?" I said in a cold bloody spirit, "Bitch when you tell me some shit like who you tired of flipping, it's like telling me you getting tired of making my money. Is that what you mean?!"

"Daddy NO," she said in an ass kissing voice!!! She continued to moan saying, "Daddy how could you say something like that? I will never get tired of giving you my all!" Testing her dedication, I said, "Okay bitch then stay down and pay that fine you just let come out your mouth!" She barely whispered out, "Yes Daddy."

Michelle had a look on her face like she was glad that she wasn't Melissa!!! Pulling up in Denny's parking lot my six-foot blonde was sitting at the table eating when I tapped my horn for her to come out. When she got inside of the car, she sat to the right side of me. Jazz was my bottom hoe. So, her spot in my game was always on the right side.

"Daddy your chicken fingers are cold. Do you want to wait 'til we get home so I could warm them up?"

"No Jazz, Michelle can have them." Michelle couldn't resist nothing I gave her, just the fact of knowing it was coming from me.

"Yes Daddy, I will eat them", she said as if I was giving her a gift.

Jazz came out of the blue and asked, "Daddy can I roll us a blunt?" I shocked her when I asked, "You need it hoe?"

"No Daddy, all I need is your Pimping. I just wanted to smoke." My hoes knew I didn't like them to ask me for nothing as if they needed it. Yes, I would allow them to smoke weed because I smoked, but for the record I was their only high and addiction, can you dig it?

Once we pulled up to Jazz room, Infinity wasn't in the lobby like I instructed her to be. I sent Jazz to her room to get the trap that she made earlier. As she was headed to her room, Infinity was coming out another room with a construction looking white guy. She spotted me and did a U-turn back to the room so that the trick wouldn't know where she was going. Less than a minute later, she was coming down the stairs with Jazz holding hands. "Daddy, I just flipped that trick for a bill fifty which makes my trap add up to five thousand and fifty dollars." I knew what she was trying to do which is make her in-laws jealous. So, I said, "look hoe, I don't need you screaming my business out loud!!!" She knew I was hip to her move and said in a non-regretful spirit, "I'm sorry Daddy, I guess I'm just excited!"

On my way to scoop the last trap for today, I said to myself, *was an hour enough time for Melissa to make her out of pocket fee?* Her phone call answered my question.

"Hi Daddy, she said in an exhausted voice. I made three hundred and thirty more dollars. Will you please come break me for what I have on me, because having all of this cash on me makes me feel uncomfortable?"

"Where are you Melissa," I asked?

"Inside a Mexican house Daddy on Jimmy Carter Boulevard."

"Okay Melissa, I'm five minutes away from Jimmy Carter, meet me in front of Sam's Gas Station."

Within five minutes I posted in front of Sam's when Melissa showed up looking like the $1550, she said she had. Michelle jumped out and let Melissa get in so she could sit in the right spot in my Pimping, which was next to her. When Melissa got in the car, she spread her legs wide open and said, "Damn my pussy sore!!!!" Jazz and Infinity was putting their trap in order for me to count it. All of my girls knew the way I liked my money, which was all big bills on top, no $1 dollar bills in my trap and make sure my money was heavy starch with no wrinkle in it.

Reaching over the seat handing me their traps at the same time, I cut on my inside car light to see what Melissa was doing. She had my trap between her legs as if my money was a hot rag to make her pussy feel better. "Break Luck Bitch," I said, "and wait until you get home to nurse on that sore cunt of yours." She just smiled and said, "Daddy, everything is in order and straighten out, here's my trap."

Riding back to the house you would have thought my hoes was in the library the way everyone was quiet. My youngest hoe Infinity broke the silence, when she asked one of her 'Test My Pimping questions.' She said being sarcastic, "Daddy, I was just sitting here thinking how you don't do nothing, but ride around all day on gasoline and dressing clean Pimping." Coming back with a cold response I said, "Bitch, how dare you say, all I do is ride around all day, doing nothing but Pimping! You sarcastic ass bitch! Find someone who can keep four hoes in check and making sure you bitches, have the proper game that will secure you to make it back to me successful and safe. Bitch, my job... everyone can't do! You got to be certified and born to pimp to do my job bitch! So, now do you really want to know what I do to make my job harder than anyone else?" Everyone was looking at me in curios, with a look on their face like, yes, please tell us. I said with confidence, "Bitch I have to think for four hoes! And to some people that's the hardest thing to do in this world!" Infinity looked at me like she hated herself for asking me a test question and said, "I'm sorry Daddy, I didn't think of it that way." Still cold on the bitch I said, "I know you didn't know better bitch cause

I'm thinking for you right now. So, sit back and stop trying to do my job bitch before you go crazy." Then, I asked everyone in the car did they want me to wake them up from the dreams we living? My bottom hoe Jazz cut me off and said, "Daddy, please don't wake me up because all of my dreams have came true!" The rest of the girls repeated the same thing and looked at Infinity with furious eyes.

Ten minutes after one, the girls and I pulled up at my plush four-bedroom townhouse in Stone Mountain, GA. I told my bottom hoe Jazz to wait in the car while I go inside and give the girls a rundown on where to work this weekend. Inside my King Size bedroom, I gave the girls a thirty-minute rundown on the areas I wanted them to work.

"Be sure to pack up enough clothes for the weekend." This wasn't my first time going out of town and leaving the girls on automatic. So, they all knew what to do and what I expected out of them when I left.

My young hoe Infinity looked like she wanted to cry every time I would leave or separate her from my Pimping. *Christ! I never should have let her feel my swipe so soon, because now it has made her slow and worry about me too much.*

While they were gathering their clothes together, I slid back outside to finish giving Jazz instructions on what I wanted her to do with the girls and her trap. She said in a disappointed voice, "Daddy, are you leaving for a long time?"

"Maybe," I said, as I watched her tear up. Then I said, "dig this Pretty Angel, Daddy has a job to do just like you all do. Now Jazz what did I tell you about letting me see them square ass feelings?"

"Daddy I'm not no square! But I'm still a woman that cares for her man like a true woman should!"

"Okay bitch! I have three more hoes who feel the same way about me like you do, maybe more! So, like I said, I don't want to see no feelings, understand?"

"Yes Daddy," she said and kissed my fist.

"Now dig this, I'm going to Pensacola, FL to knock me another hoe!"

Jazz responded back with confidence, "Daddy, Good luck!"

I said back with a motivating attitude, "Wish the bitch luck, not me. I'm going to leave the Lincoln for you to drive yourself and the girls to work. And Jazz you already know I don't want you riding around putting miles on my wheels and not y'all heels. So, park that car as soon as you hit the track. You Understand?"

"Yes Daddy," she said smiling.

"Also, I want you to get everyone's trap including yours, and send it through Western Union to me the next morning. Be sure to put twenty-five hundred in my name and the other twenty-five hundred in Mom's name.

Chapter 8

Jazz was the bottom hoe in my stable and the one I can depend on to handle my business. I always felt like if Jazz would ever leave me the farthest, she would go would be to the Mental Ward. I had broke Jazz for over a million dollars and pimped two nice houses out of her cunt, so I wasn't worried about Jazz going anywhere other than the crazy house, if she would have ever left. I wasn't the kind of Pimp who would keep an account on how long a hoe stayed with me, I kept count on what I broken her for. Same way I didn't count the heads in my stable I counted the bread. You see some Pimps would have over five girls working for him but can't really say that he has one of his hoes in check. The Game characterize them type of Pimps as Simps.

Once the girls finished packing, I told them all to come in the living room so we could smoke some rooster and watch this movie called, *Carlito's Way* with Al-Pacino. During the middle of the movie, I heard something strange as if some pigs were in my house, but instead of it being pigs, the strange sound was my hoes all snoring at the same time. *I thought to myself, what a great Pimp I am.* There was all of my hoes laying on one another like real sisters. I unfolded my recliner love seat and went in my private room to think. One thing I know for sure in this game is when a Pimp hoes are getting along and they like one another, he has created a beautiful family!!!

Early in the morning, in my sleep, I could hear someone knocking at my bedroom door. Waking up as if I was never sleep, I said in an awaken voice, "Come In." It was my youngest hoe Infinity dress in nothing but her panties. "Good Morning Daddy was you sleep?" I told one of my believable lies, "No hoe I was thinking. Now what do you want dressed like you ready for me to send you to work?"

She said while flirting, "Daddy I'm going to miss you this weekend. Can I please feel you before you leave? You haven't touched me in two months. Please Daddy! At least let me taste you?" I knew she was a nympho and worse than a dog in heat when it came to sex. So, I allowed her to keep touching and raping herself imagining me inside of her. Breaking her concentration was a knock at the door. "Come In," I said as my bottom hoe Jazz seen Infinity a piece from being naked. "Oh, I'm sorry Daddy," as if she had interrupted Infinity and my groove. "Sorry for what?" I said. "You just in time to say what you have to say and take the freak with you." Infinity looked as if I hurt her feelings. My Pimping was based on devotions not emotions. Stumbling out of the room hurt just as much as anger, Infinity slammed my bedroom door with an attitude.

I'm hip that was her way of trying to get me to show her some attention, so I ignored her methods and let her feel mines. Jazz was still standing there dressed in an eye catching see through Coogi dress.

"We're going to need some money to get the game started this weekend Daddy," Jazz said.

"Okay give me a minute to get myself together, I'll be out in a second Jazz."

After taking over an hour to get myself together, all of the girls were in the living room laughing and joking about the tricks they have robbed and dated. Soon as I stepped in the room everyone immediately got quiet.

"Okay ladies here's the rundown for the weekend. Infinity you and Michelle are going to play off Jimmy Carter Blvd. And Jazz I want you and Melissa to play Shallow Ford Road. I don't want no hoe calling me about a situation that you can hoe your own way out of. If it gets hot with the police where you at, switch spots but don't stop working. Everyone know what I want you to do in the morning with your trap right?" Infinity cut me off as if she didn't know.

"No Daddy, what do you want us to do? Send it off to you?" Infinity didn't like giving her trap to the next hoe to give to me, so she was hoping I said yes. Instead, I said, "Bitch you know what I want you to do with my money. All of you give your trap to Jazz. Take out what you need to keep going, but I don't want no one coming in with less than a thousand, Understand?"

"Yes Daddy," they all said at the same time. They all grabbed their things, then lined up in one line kissing my fist before they left.

An hour later I was pulling up to Goldy Locs hotel. I spotted the same pretty Indian looking bitch walking with a stud who looked like King Kong. *I wonder was she his banana for today? The way he had her all wrapped up, you can tell he would have fought everyone in the jungle to protect her.* Laughing to myself, I picked up my phone to call Goldy letting him know that

I was in the parking lot. Five minutes later he came down dressed like he was in high pursuit for a Prostitute.

I popped my trunk so that he could put his luggage in the back. I noticed the way he was bobbing his head to the words to this song called, *Break Yourself Bitch* by Players Choice. He got into the car with plenty of spirit and motivation.

"Say Mane, I'm ready to have me a Hoe! I really do appreciate you Mac Goldie for putting my pimping back on the road."

"No problem baby, this is the scene I love to see, when two Pimps hit the road and go cross country pimping. This is going to tell what you have in you and what you don't."

Chapter 9

It was close to two o'clock when we finished gassing up and on our way to Pensacola, Fl. Goldy and I drove for about 20 minutes quietly listening to the best of classic music by Curtis Mayfield, Bobby Womack, Willie Hutch and The Spinners. He brought a couple of rap CDs like, Too $hort, Tupac, The Ghetto Boys and my homeboys Eightball and MJG. I can tell from the look on Goldy Locs face that he was excited about leaving Atlanta. I pushed mute on my remote and said, "So Goldy, tell me, when was the last time you exercised your pimping in another state?" He said shamefully, "To be honest Goldie it's been over two years! Atlanta has always been a good city to work and knock a hoe. I believe that I got too content with what I was making and wouldn't go anywhere else. Now Goldie, it's like I feel Atlanta trying to starve me for depending on it so long." I cut him off saying, "Nah Pimping, don't put it on Atlanta. Atlanta been good for years, but you and I know the game we play is to be played "International." Goldy Locs rubbed his chin looked at me smiling saying, "You right Mac Goldie, this game is a road game Jack, and that's what we doing now, putting it back on the road."

So, tell me Mac Goldie, did you come up on all your hoes in the same city or in different states?"

"Nah, Pimping, all my hoes came from different states. My bottom hoe Jazz is from Indianapolis, she was in her second year of college dancing at this titty bar called *Shannon's.* The only white bitch in the club surrounded by nothing but Pimps, hoes and tricks. I came in the club that night and gave her a healthy conversation along with my number. For the next couple of days, we hung out and a situation brought us together. I turned her out into doing whatever I wanted her to do. My thickest hoe is named Michelle, she also was in college, but a neighborhood slut to her community. I knocked her from a dope boy who wasn't doing nothing but fucking on her. My youngest bitch name Infinity is from my city Memphis, Tenn. She was half hoeing and trying to gang bang at the same time. She left her boyfriend who she thought was a Pimp until he met me. And my last hoe name is Melissa, she's from Kansas City."

Goldy Locs looked at me and said, "Damn Pimping, you basically turned all of your hoes out, right?"

I responded back with dedication saying, "Not only did I turn them out, but I also put them hoes life on right."

"Mane I can dig it," is all Goldy Locs could say as he shook his head as if I was blessed.

It was five minutes till six o'clock when we made it to this small town called Crestview, FL. I was known in this town for breaking up relationships, marriages and families. Every time I came through here, I would leave with someone's wife, girlfriend or daughter. Even the sheriffs would tip their hats when they seen me in town. I had one sheriff tell me, "You should come in town more and change some of these girls life."

I switched conversation and start telling Goldy Locs about a bitch named Stephanie who was a correctional officer in Georgia. She fell in love with my Pimping and helped me escape from prison.

"This is where Stephanie family live," I said. Goldy Locs looked at me out of curiosity and said, "Where do Stephanie live?"

"The last time I heard Goldy Locs, they said the bitch was in a Mental Ward!!!" Goldy Locs said sounding shocked, "Damn Pimping you drove the bitch crazy? Are you sure you want to pull over in this town?" He said with fear in his eyes. "The crazy bitch might be out and have enough sense now to kill us both!" I laughed so hard until my stomach was hurting.

Then I said, "You have nothing to worry about Goldy, the bitch would rather kill herself before she will me. Can you dig it?" He hesitated then said with a counterfeit response, "I guess I can dig it."

I rode through this neighborhood where a lot of loose bitches be hanging out and smoking weed. When Goldy Locs seen the scene, he felt more comfortable and ready to exercise his macking.
I said with confidence, "Goldy, this is where you going to catch you a hoe. It's going to be plenty of them little freaks in the club later tonight. By the time we go check in a hotel room and re- groom ourselves, it should be time to get the game started."
"Dig That!" Goldy Locs said with enthusiasm.

Chapter 10

It was close to 12 o'clock when Goldy and I woke up from the nap we took when we checked in the room. I had missed over twenty calls from my phone and pager. "Christ!" I said as I called back the last number that called me.

It was my bottom hoe Jazz, "Daddy, I been trying to call you for hours! Are you okay?"

"Of course, I'm okay, why wouldn't I be?" I said to her as if I didn't appreciate her concern!

"I'm sorry Daddy but the girls and I was worried. We all was trying to give you our rundown for today but no one could reach you."

"Where are the girls now?" I asked.

"Everyone is here with me," Jazz said.

"And where is that bitch!"

"I'm sorry Daddy, at my room. Okay good! Give me a rundown on the business," I said.

"Well Daddy, I haven't got any of the girls money yet, but my score is $2340. I took $100 out to pay for my room." I asked her out of curiosity, "Is any of that good money hot?" She smirked then said, "No Daddy, I flat back for everything! Daddy, it feels like my pussy is swollen!"

"Put the next hoe on the phone." I said as if I didn't hear what she had said. Infinity sounded excited when she got on the phone speaking, "Hi Daddy."

"What's up hoe," I answered her back. "You sound excited I know you have a nice trap for Daddy, right?"

"Daddy, the track was slow and plus I couldn't steal anything. My trap is only $850. But Daddy the reason I sound so excited because I'm glad to hear from you and plus I miss you," she said as if I been gone for years!

"Hoe, I've only been gone for twelve hours and you talking about you miss me! You better get your mind tight and my money right if you ever want to see me again." I said in an icy tone!

I heard the phone drop to the floor and Infinity stomping like she always does when she want some attention. My next hoe Melissa got on the phone like the mature hoe I raised her to be, "Hi Daddy."

"Hello Super Star," I answered.

"Daddy, it was slow, but I still pulled $1,075 out of my ass."

Giving her my Pimp support I said, "Dig this Baby Fox, you are a Star. And no matter how slow the track gets you still going to make something happen. Have you spoke with your kids or mother," I asked out of concern?

"No Daddy, I was going to wait until you came back to call."

"Okay cool, pass your sister Michelle the phone." Sounding like she just robbed a bank Michelle said excitedly, "Daddy, guess what?"

"Bitch, I don't have time to be guessing! Now tell me what's your score?" Still sounding excited she said, "Daddy, I crept a wallet with $825 in it! Plus, I flat back for $1100. My score Daddy for today is nineteen hundred, twenty-four dollars and sixty-five cent!" Smiling to myself I said, "Damn Miss Loyalty, you got to be the first hoe I've had to share the thousands, hundreds and cents with a Pimp!" I could hear her blushing through the phone before she said, "Daddy, I just want you to have every dollar and cent that I hoe for."

Waiting for a response Michelle asked me, "Daddy, aren't you proud of me?"

"Sure, Baby girl, I'm proud to know that all the time and patience I put into you paid off. Keep up the good work. You might be one of my players I take to the Super Bowl." Giggling thru the phone she said, "Daddy, I want to be your MVP you take to the Super Bowl and win the game!"

Every hoe in my stable wanted to be the hoe I considered as my *Most Valuable Prostitute.*

"Pass your sister Jazz, back the phone Michelle," I said. "Jazz, I want you to get the girls money and send it off like I told you."

"Yes Daddy, I will." I was satisfied with the way the girls had handle my business.

When I hung up the phone from the girls, Goldy was outside talking to two beautiful snows who had just checked into the hotel. Goldy looked over at me and said to the two girls, "I want you young ladies to meet someone. This is my twin brother, Mac Goldie." Both of the Hollywood looking stars smiled and said at the same time, "Oh My Gosh! You guys are twins and dress like Movie Stars! What do you guys do, rap?" Goldy smiled and said, "You're right about us being Stars, but we're not rappers. We them guys that you always wanted to meet but your family warned you to stay away from." One of the girls said, "Drug Dealers?"

"No Mrs. Right, you wrong again," I said. Before she could ask another question, I cut her off asking, "How old are you two?"

"I'm eighteen and my friend is seventeen."

"Why?" Is what the one that was 17 years old said. I cut in saying, "Because you not old enough to hear men like us talk. Now keep living for 'bout three more years and I will make it my business to come and raise you from there." The young girls felt offended and said, "I'm not fucking young, I do what the fuck I want!! Now I get it! You guys are Pimps!" Goldy looked at me and said, "Sounds like a young hooker to me that knows her kind." We both laughed as we got into the car then I said, "Say Mane how bout we head to the club where some legal bitches are!!"

"I can dig that," Goldy said.

I was running down to Goldy on how many underage girls was in the town looking for a way out of here. I push mute again on my radio and said, "But Goldy one thing you will know about my pimping is, "I don't fuck with babies or underage girls." I continued to say, "that was my first lesson in the game, "never pimp on an underage girl! They must be old enough to make a decision to fuck with me!"

"I Can dig it," reaching his hand out before answering Goldy said, "Mac Goldie, I really dig the shit out your Pimping. I don't believe in that pedophile shit either! That's why I'm whoreless now Mac Goldie. The few bitches that I had an interview with was either too young or wanted me to cut a deal with her." Before he could say another word the crowd from the club caught his attention leaving him speechless! He said excitedly, "Lord have mercy on me, damn Goldie! Look at all these white bitches, black bitches, Spanish bitches, CHRIST! I've never seen no shit like this before!"

As I said earlier, my pimping was known in this town, so every hustler and bitch knew my car when they seen it. Looking for my VIP parking spot I seen one available in front of the club. I parked my pimping and left the motor running while Goldy and I cracked our windows to hear the crowd conversation. Goldy paralyzed his eyes on a cute chubby snow standing on his passenger side. When he stepped out the car the whole parking lot pointed and stared at the hypnotize white silk suit Goldy had on. Un- hypnotizing their eyes when I step out in my midnight black Zenyatta Suit. Looking like a reflection of Goldy's shadow. You can hear the squares and hustlers saying, "Damn, who are they?" Stephanie's brother named Rick recognize me and shouted through the crowd, "Oh Shit, you niggas better cuff your girls, cause a real Pimp is back in Town." Slick Rick was a Pimp's friend, and he knew every baller, hustlers and loose bitch in town. Smiling like a Shirley Temple slave he embraced me with a miss you hug and I'm glad to see you shake. I showed love back then said, "Say Rick, I want you to meet a good friend and family of mines, Goldy Locs." Rick reached his hand out while still smiling and said, "Nice to meet you Goldy." Then said, "Your name Goldie too? Damn you two look like twins! Are you a Pimp?" Goldy couldn't do nothing but smile and said to Rick, "Let's just say, it's some more of it in town."

Rick invited us in the club so that he could show off what everyone wanted to see. This was his way of building up his reputation in the town.

When the DJ seen us, he stopped the music and said, "Aw shit, we have some Boss Players in the house tonight. All the way from ATL. Mac Goldie told me to tell all you hoes to get your money right if you want to leave with a Pimp tonight!"

Slick Rick had the security escort us to the VIP room. Outside stood a group of bitches in a line waiting to be interviewed. Showing all of his 32 gold teeth Goldy was in good Pimp spirit. Slick Rick wanted to show Goldy around and introduce him to the next candidate. I looked across from me and seen this pretty young freak reckless eyeballing my Pimping. So, I told her with a cold stare to come over. I read her lips asking, "Who Me?" She switched all the way from her table to mines looking like a young Foxy Brown as she approached me saying, "Was you talking to me?" She stood there wide legged while sipping on a class of walk me down. I replied, "No I wasn't talking to you! As a matter of fact, I didn't say anything to you. But since you made the move before anyone else could, I'm talking to you now, have a seat." She sat in front on me with her legs busted wide open advertising what's on display. I ignored what she was trying to do and asked, "What's your name Hot Mama?" She got offended and said, "I'm not Hot!" "Calm down lil' mama maybe you misinterpret what I meant. My terminology for hot mama means you ready for the game."

"What Game," she asked now looking serious and sober?

"Pimping and Hoeing," I said to see her reaction. She leaped to her feet saying, "Nigga you have me fucked up! I'm not a hoe!" I said to her back, "I'm sure you not a hoe, but you have some hoeing in you baby, you just need the right man to bring it out. But dig this baby, you can't qualify with an attitude like yours." She looked as if she wanted to pour the rest of her drink on me, but she knew what was going to come behind it if she did. So instead, she just rolled her eyes and left my presence.

When I went outside Goldy had the same chubby girl posted up with him against the car. In one of his hands, he had her identification and the other hand he had a small trap. When he seen me, he made the big freak go to the back of the car and wait so that him and I could talk. I seen the cop in his eyes before saying anything. Then he said, "Dig this Goldie, this young bitch is 18 years old, just graduated, working at Burger King but ready to quit and get out this slow ass town." He continued saying, she broke herself for this gold necklace with a hundred and forty dollars. This is her driving license. Mac Goldie I'm ready to go back to the "A" and pimp a car out this big bitch!!" I felt comfortable with his rundown as we left that same night with Goldy new bitch. The whole six hours on our way back Goldy sat in the back seat with his new game lacing her up with his rules and instructions.

Chapter 11

We came to a stop so that Goldy's hoe can use the restroom and also get some gas. While she was inside of the store Goldy was giving me another rundown on her life. He said, "Goldie this little bitch is the only child that her parents have, and her father is a drunk and rapist which is why she was ready to leave Crestview, Fl. He continued to say, "the bitch can't wait to show me how much she appreciates me! Mac Goldie do me a favorite and test my bitch when she get back inside the car. I gave her instructions to only talk to me and keep her head down to the floor.

Soon as she got back into the car, she gave Goldy the change left from the bill he gave her, then she turned her head the opposite way toward me. I waited a cool 30 minutes before I tried to play her out of pocket. I pressed mute on the remote to the radio and said, "Bonnie, will you look inside that back seat pocket and pass me my CD case?" She flinched like she was about to, but Goldy rules must have reminded the bitch to stay in pocket. I still was determined to get her out of pocket as I said, "listen Bonnie, Goldy and I are blood brothers, it's going to be times I see you working, and you might need some help. Now in order for us to help one another we must communicate. I'm not a stranger, we all family. Now pass me that CD case bitch before I put your ass out my car!" Instead of listening to me, the bitch took both of her hands covering up her ears to avoid from listening to me. I looked over to Goldy and said, "Look like she have some respect for you Goldy." He just kept his head straight forward saying, "yeah we'll see how this bitch add up on the blade."

It was twenty minutes after seven when we made it back to Atlanta. Pulling up in front of Goldy's hotel he instructed his game to go to room 242 and wait on him to come up. She only had the outfit that was on her body and the game Goldy had put in her. But I knew, before the day was over

Goldy will be having her looking like a Friday night lick!!

Once she had gotten out the car and went upstairs, Goldy said to me, "Goldie Mane, I want to thank you baby, for believing in me and making it possible to have this bitch." I smiled and said, "dig this Goldy, I know a spot you can work your bitch to make sure you get your choosing fee out of her. It's *called Mexican Land.* They're going to empty out their wallets to that thick white bitch!" Rubbing his hands together and smiling at the same time he said, "Goldie, we will be ready at two o'clock. I'm ready to pimp me some transportation out of the bitch cunt!" Shaking my hands once again, Goldy gave me a hug and said, "you a Blessing Goldie, see you at two.

Leaving Goldy's hotel room, I noticed that my gas hand was on E and I needed to get some gas along with a swisher sweet to roll me a fat blunt! As I was pulling into Amco Gas Station, I seen this dingy barefoot white girl in the parking lot trying to hoe. She couldn't be no older than twenty-years old by her looks and immature moves. I can also tell she had a drug habit by the way she kept moving her mouth. Before I got out my car, I stayed hid behind my tint to peep her next move. Just as I thought. She was headed toward my car as if I was a trick. What she didn't know, was that she was walking up on a man, who was a Pimp.

Before she could approach the car, I let down the back window so that she can get a scent of what she was about to get into. You can tell she must have smelled my pimping because she immediately froze to see who was driving. When I stepped out the car, she seemed to have some respect for the game the way she broke her ankles trying to get away from me. I thought to myself, *I wonder how bad her habit was and if I was able to save her.* Her next move answered my thoughts. A young drug dealer walked up and sold her a sack of narcotics. *Damn, a good hoe gone bad.*

After filling up on gas and rolling me a blunt I dived into the early morning traffic, swimming my way 20 West to catch up on me some Pimp rest. The traffic was jam packed on highway 20 West, so I had to exit my way off on Martin Luther King. While riding, I thought about the way Goldy and I cut into one another through a confused faggot bitch. To an outsider it seemed like Goldy lost his hoe, but on the inside of the game the hoe is the one that lost.
Especially, when she had a good Pimp! Really when hoes jump from one Pimp to the next one, all she does is make it possible for Pimps to meet one another and hopefully have a relationship like Goldy and were building.

In this game, hoes constantly come and go. They sometimes pay to stay, then be on their way to the next Pimp. Hoes are not promised to be with you forever, that's why you have to Pimp as much as you can real fast before the hoe go silly. The more you get them to invest, the harder it is for them to leave. Still keep this in mind, no matter how much she gives you or how long she stays, she still will leave you lonely, hoeless and broke. Any true Pimp knows when a hoe leaves, she opens up the door for the next hoe to come through. A Pimp never let a hoe leave him broken hearted. Instead, you celebrate when she leaves. It gives the next hoe a chance to become a Star in "Pimping and Hoeing."

Chapter 12

Twenty minutes before 8 o'clock I finally pulled up at my townhouse in Stone Mountain, Ga. I knew the girls was at their hotel room like I instructed them to be, and this was my only time for me to be alone. But before I could get comfortable, I had to call my bottom hoe Jazz, and let her know that I was home and not to send the money off through Western Union. Before I could make the call, I was receiving a call from Goldy.

"Hello, what's happenin' Mac Goldie?" Goldy asked me still sounding full of spirit.

"What's going on Goldy," I said.

"I was just checking to make sure you made it home safe in all that traffic?" Feeling grateful I said, "I sure did make it in safely Goldy. Thanks for the concern!" He started telling me how him and his hoe have already hit a track and that he made sure she was laced up with the plays to win. "Pimp on Pimping," is what I said. I felt more excited than he was.

After talking to Goldy on the phone, I wasn't sleepy anymore. His rundown gave me plenty energy to get my game started for today.

I called Jazz as if I was her morning alarm clock to get up.

"Hello" she said in a sleepy tone.

"What's up hoe? It's time to get your big, long pretty ass up!"

"Hi Daddy!" This time she said in a more awaken tone! "What time is it Daddy?"

"Bitch, didn't I just say it was time for you to get your ass up! Now get your ass up and call me at the apartment when you get yourself together." This time sounding excited she called back saying, "Daddy are you in town?"

"No hoe. I'm in your dream. I just happen to be in the town you dreaming in. Did you get everyone's trap together like I instructed you to do?"

"Yes, Daddy. Infinity acted like she wasn't giving up her trap, she said she wanted to put her trap in your hands herself. Daddy, she finally gave it to me when I said well,

I'll let you deal with daddy yourself. Daddy, I'm tired of Infinity nasty ass attitude. She thinks she's you and can talk to me any kind of way. I'm trying my best to respect your pimping but Daddy, I can't see none of your Pimping in her." Before she said another word I said, "check yourself right now Hoe! If you want to make a move on my Pimping don't use this bitch for a reason! None of you hoes is a necessity to a Pimp!! Now get your ass up, go pick up your sisters and bring everyone back over here!" "Yes Daddy," she said in a sorry tone. I fired up me a blunt to relax my nerve and to also smoke up on an appetite.

The next phone call was from my son, Lil' G.

"Hello," I said.

"What's up Dad," Lil G asked me then started telling me about an ex-hoe of mine named Bonnie. "Dad, I saw her working on Lamar Ave, when I called her name, she looked at me like she didn't know who I was. Then I saw her jump in this

White Mercedes with a black guy who was dress like you." G, asked me out of concern, "Daddy, is Bonnie still with you, or have she got with someone else?"

"No son, Bonnie is not with me. She left a month ago and now is working for this Pimp name Mac Dee. The reason she didn't speak with you son was because a hoe is only allowed to speak to business not pleasure. So, now you see when I use to tell you not to get too comfortable with these hoes cause they will be here one day with you and gone tomorrow with the next player.

Lil G was only 10 years old at the time, but he was laced up with knowledge and understanding about the game. He was my only child, and we kicked it together like we were brothers or best friends. Every color suit I put on, he had one too! But he was far from wanting to become a Pimp. He was more of a rapper mix with a player. The one thing that I respected about G, is that he never went to school or around his friends telling my business. The hoes loved Lil' G as if he was me. But he built his own relationship with them. He will rap for them and also bring out the childish ways they still had in them. They will act so silly around G. I remember one time I let Lil' G ride out of town with the girls to Atlanta. The girls told me how he was trying to imitate me telling them to crack the window if they smoked any weed. And when they all checked into the hotel G said, "I want a bed to myself like my dad always sleep. So, you all going to sleep in that bed and I'm sleeping over here by myself and shut that damn Door!" When the girls gave me that rundown on Lil' G I thought to myself, *maybe G do have a little Pimping in him.*

During the Winter, Fall, and Spring, Lil' G stayed with his mother to attend school. But once school was out, he was all mines for the summer. We would go from state to state enjoying ourselves on the beaches and all the park adventures. I loved to see Lil' G happy and experience the fun I didn't have when I was his age. I instilled the same values in Lil' G that I instilled in the girls. Which is to be responsible, respectful, loyal, confident, patient, and how to treat people the way you will want someone to treat you. These are values that are priceless, and you couldn't buy them with all the money in the world! In the Game, it's what us Pimps call a hoe "Life Support."

It was 9:30am when Jazz and the girls pulled up to the apartment. I could tell Jazz was still hurt from what I said to her earlier because you can still see the 'I'm sorry' look on her face. But the rest of the girls was excited and ready to see their man they haven't seen in 12 hours, Their Daddy. Jazz asked, "Daddy, may I speak with you in private?" She wanted to give me the girls and her trap that they made while I was gone.

Before she handed me the money she said regretfully, "Daddy, I'm sorry for making you upset earlier, will you please forgive me and allow me to make it up to you later when I get down?" I paused before saying anything then said, "come here hoe. Remember this for future reference, in this game the only person you need to be concerned about is me! Don't let another hoe steal your belief and faith in me, you dig?"

"Yes Daddy," she said as tears was rolling down her beautiful face. I continued to say, "It's going to be plenty hoes that try to knock you for your position and you in my Pimping. But you must stay focused Jazz understand?"

"Yes Daddy," she said using that same sellable smile I told her to sell in the streets. That's when she passed me a six thousand, one hundred- and eighty-nine-dollars trap and said, "Daddy, I didn't take out what we need to get started for today because I didn't know you was coming back so soon."

"It's cool baby, I will give the girls what they need when I talk with them.

Listen close Jazz, I want you to keep your eyes open for this chubby white hoe. She's a fresh hoe to a Pimp partner of mines. If you should see her making any wrong moves or doing anything that will hurt my Pimp friend trap be sure to contact me! Also, when she sees you, I want you to put on your best performance showing her how real hoes get down for their man!"

"Yes Daddy, but Daddy what if she start asking me choosing question, you know about us?"

"Just tell the hoe, she's going to have to choose up with someone else because I don't believe in taking a Pimp friend of mines last hoe. The bitch should know to get back in pocket. Also hip the Mexicans that a fresh hoe is on the set who is a virgin in the game." Jazz smile turned to a frown and said, "But Daddy, isn't that going to interfere with my money?"

I said, "hoe, if you let a first day hoe block my game then you need to be broke!"

"I'm not Daddy." She again smiling.

"Roll up a couple of blunts Jazz, I'll be in there in a minute."

This was my first time telling my hoe to watch out for another hoe who wasn't in the family. I didn't believe in knocking a good Pimp for his only hoe unless he wasn't proper or a true pimp friend that I had a relationship with. Even if the confused bitch chose me with a respectable trap, I would get the money up off her, but she had to go back or get going.

Chapter 13

When I came in the living room the girls were smoking and cracking jokes on how they keep tricks broke. "What are you devious hoes talking about?" I said.

"Tricks and money Daddy." My youngest hoe Infinity answered.

"Daddy, can I work on Steward Ave, today?"

"No baby, I'm sending you and Michelle down to Daytona Beach to work the Race Event."

"Today Daddy?" Infinity said excited!!

"No Hoe, next week. Of course, today. Now get on the phone and found out the next flight leaving out today." You would thought this bitch did a flip to the phone the way she skipped the couch to the phone. She knew every time she went to work major events, she will make over ten thousand in cash and steal some nice valuables to bring to me. As I said before, Infinity was a lucky hoe when it came down to my pimping. She hung up the phone as if someone had died.

"What did they say Hoe?" I asked, because of the way she was looking. She said sadly, "Daddy, they only had one flight that left out for today and it left at 8:00 o'clock this morning." She continued to say, "Damn Daddy, I wanted to bring you back a Bank Roll!!" I gave her a counterfeit smile and said, "hoe stop all that popping it. You still have a chance to make that same bank roll you talking about in this city." I continued to say, "all you have to do is take my game with you to work." She just smiled and said out of belief, "Believe that Daddy."

Michelle was also excited about going to Daytona until she still wanted to work with Infinity.

"Daddy, can I work with Infinity today?" Looking at her in disbelief I said, "Since when you two want to work together?" She answered, "Daddy I love working with Infinity and putting down that 2 on 1 press on a trick that you showed us." To convince me, they both hug one another, trying to persuade my decision. I can tell by their actions that their feelings was fake for each other, but to show them that I was a better actor than they were actress' I said, "I'm going to see how you hoes work together today in the Wolf Chase Apartments. Infinity, I want you to work the front and you Michelle the back. When you both finish from working your area meet another in the middle and team up with the 2 on 1 game."

"Yes Daddy." They both giggled at the same time from the buzz of the weed. By this time, it was 11:15am. The girls or me had anything to eat yet so we all got dressed for lunch. Our favorite lunch spot, "The Sunset Soul Food Place" on Glenwood Road. I remember the first time we all went there to eat, when the girls sat at one table and I sat at the other one by myself. This pretty little waitress came over to see if I needed anything to drink. Before she could ask me anything my bottom hoe Jazz cut her off saying,

"Sorry Sweetie, anything my daddy need we will get it for him." Jazz continue to say, "the only thing we're going to need help with is getting him some more money. "Now do you have anything to give him?" The young pretty innocent waitress never seen a stable of hoes down for one man the way my girls were. She said sarcastically, "excuse me, I was just trying to earn a tip."

"Well, we just gave you one, get with some Pimping." All the girls said while laughing at the little square bitch. Never once did I lift my head up from eating. My Game had already hipped the young bitch on how she can serve me.

When we finish from eating it was close to 12 o'clock and 2 hours away from hooking up with Goldy. I decided to give him a call just to see how things was going with him and his Pimping. Answering the phone after five rings Goldy finally picked up saying, "Hey, what's happenin' Mac Goldie! Mane I was just about to call you and give you a rundown on this hoe of mines." He started popping it on how the hoe is doing more hoeing than tip toeing! "Mac Goldie I'm already four hundred and some change out of this hoe pussy, and today just begun." To show his appreciation he asked me, "Goldie please let a Pimp buy you lunch today!"

I was flattered for his offer and said, "Goldy I truly appreciate the offer, but the girls and I just had lunch at The Sunset. I was calling to see was you ready, and what's your location?" He answered back in good spirit, "Of course, I'm ready to bend some blocks with a Pimp and check some hoe money. I'm riding through Five Points now getting ready to scoop the bitch. Where are you Mac Goldie?"

"I'm on the expressway headed South to drop two of my hoes off in Mid-town, and the rest of them on Buford Highway. Asking out of concern I asked Goldy, "How are you getting around Goldy?" He answered back, "I'm in a taxi who is a good friend of mines."

"Okay cool. When you finish from scooping your hoe, have him drop you off on North Druid Hills at the Denny's restaurant."

"Dig That." Goldy said, as we hung up the phone.

Making my exit off on 10th Street, I gave my hoe Melissa instructions on where I wanted her to work which was down Ponce De Leon. I also instructed her to do business with no one but her kind, "WHITES."

My reason for telling my hoe this was so she will be safe and not in the mix of a gorilla or any other slick hustler. I instilled in the girls head to do business with "Short Dicks and Big Money" not "Big Dicks and Small Money." Asking for a couple of dollars to buy a soda Melissa said, "Daddy, do you want me to let my trick know to come get me from the track?"

"Sure, just make sure once you finish from flipping him to get back down on the same street." Dropping her off in front of Krispy

Cream Donuts she was placed on the clock. Before leaving the strip, I saw this Pimp named Hollywood dropping his game off on the track. I met Hollywood through a pimp name Sugar Ray. They both would work their girls inside escorts and titty bars. Which was a surprise to me because I never seen them work their girls on the concrete.

Popping his collar and stomping his feet at the same time he was full of "Pimp Spirit." I greeted him with the same spirit saying, "What's happening Hollywood? It's been a long time since I seen you. How is the game treating you?"
Showing all of his pearly white teeth he answered back saying, "I can't complain Mac Goldie just a lot of these suckers trying to get their foot wet in the game we live. But other than that, how the life been treating you? You still starving these other Pimps with all that money you checking from them white hoes? How many heads you have now Goldie? Around 10?"

I popped my collar and said, "Now Hollywood, you know I don't count heads. I count the bread that I'm getting from each head. But for the record, I'm four deep. Forty toes on the concrete. Yea Mane, you best believe my pimping is alive in these hoes I have! Dig this though Hollywood, I'm on my way to scoop up Goldy Locs. Him and I went to Pensacola Fl, and he knock him a "Pink Toe." He got the bitch down right now as we speak standing up for his pimping!!" Hollywood looked at me with a look on his face of relief. He knew Goldy, and what Goldy had been going through for some time now.

He said, "Mane I sure hope Goldy know, he has a true friend who has his back, and that's you Goldie."

"I appreciate that Hollywood. I might have his back, but hoe better have his front. I fuck with Pimps that doing some Pimping. By the way Hollywood, have you heard from my homeboy Scooby?"

"Yeah Mane, me, Pimp Scooby, Sir Charles, Cash and the rest of the fellows be hanging out at the Chocolate City. That's the new track."

"Dig that Hollywood. Goldy and I will be by later to see what's loose and need to be tighten up."

He smiled then said, "make sure you bring them white hoes." I caught the pass he threw at me and threw it back saying, "you sure you want me to bring my MVP'S? Because if I do, somebody is not going to get no money that morning." We both laughed and agreed to meet later at the Chocolate City. Not realizing how fast time had passed it was going on 2 o'clock. So, I jumped back in traffic to drop off Michelle and Infinity.

Looking in my rear-view mirror my young hoe Infinity was in a trance watching me. I wonder how long this hoe was going to last. Looking for love in the wrong way. She was becoming obsessive and too possessive. That's why it's not healthy to have sex with your hoes too often. It makes them slow not focus and she starts to worry about what you doing too much.

Once I dropped them off, I had another talk with Jazz, but this time on a bottom hoe prospective. She knew whenever I wanted her to sit in the front with me is when I caress her hoe emotions with my Pimp devotions.

"Listen Jazz, you been down with me for five years now, and you know I usually don't keep count on how long a hoe stay down with me. I keep count of all the values and qualities that I Pimp out of you. You've been more than a hoe in my life, but an angel as well. We still have a lot of trials and tribulations to face, but together we can conquer anything the game bring our way. Jazz, you got to have me in you baby to conquer these trials you going to face."

She cut me off before I could say another word with her tears and said, "but Daddy, you are me. I don't know nothing else but you." I dried her damp face with some more of my charm words and finesse.

"I know I am baby, but you got to feel this way everyday God wakes you up. There's going to be some cloudy days and dark nights that may seem like nothing could motivate you. That's when you must have that belief. Do you understand me Jazz?" "Yes Daddy," she said as tears continued to roll down her face without her permission. The more I was macking, the more she was acting. Over the years Jazz and I been together we became great actors and actress. But this wasn't a movie, this was reality and the life we lived.

After macking to Jazz for over 30 minutes she was full of motivation and ready to bring me the world back from between her legs. I seen a for sure two thousand dollars trap coming back with her later that night. She cut in asking, "Daddy, what about the fresh hoe you were telling me about? Do you want me to converse with her, or maybe show her how to move around?"

"Hoe, I said keep your eyes open, not your mind focused on what that bitch doing!!" I continued to say, "you don't have to show her any moves other then what a hoe supposed to be doing, which is getting a Pimp's money, you Understand?"

"Yes Daddy," she said with a look on her face as if I killed her motivation. But all I was doing is using one of my methods a Pimp used on his hoes. Tear her down, then build her back up with some spirit before she goes to work. A hoe spirit should always be up lifted at work, because if it's not, it could affect your money. So, to put her spirit back on cloud nine I smiled and said, "kiss my fist and gain some strength my beautiful hoe." She smiled and then embraced my fist with emotions and said, "I Love You Daddy and I'm always going to be down for your crown." I pressed play with the remote and we both sat back listening to Curtis Mayfield sing the "Do Be You and Do Be Down."

Chapter 14

After I finish from talking to Jazz, I dropped her off in front of Sam's Gas Station on Jimmy Carter Blvd. Once Jazz got out the car, I noticed on the side of me was a pretty blonde, white girl at the red light staring at me. She acted as if she was mesmerized in a thought and didn't notice that the light had turned green. I shot pass her, hoping she would follow me to the next red light so I c o u l d get her information and maybe later an interview. Just her luck, next light had turn red. When she pulled up on the side of me the bitch was looking straight forward and wouldn't look at me. *Ain't this a bitch, oh well it's her loss not mines.*

Ten minutes later, I was pulling up at Denny's where I saw Goldy fresh hoe, hoeing in the parking lot. As soon as she saw my car, she immediately went the opposite way. I just smiled and said to myself, *yes, I like Goldy.* He definitely is a true bonified Pimp! This hoe hasn't been to sleep since we left Pensacola. This is what a true stomp down hoe does when she wants to see her man come up in the game.

Here comes Goldy looking like the Pimp I was ready to go Pimping with! He gave his hoe a pimp signal to start coming towards the car. You would have thought that she was a season hoe the way she moved with loyalty, respect and dedication. She was only a turn-out just under some proper pimping. I stepped out the car before Goldy could get in, greeting him with a "Pimp Shake" and a brethren hug. We rapped for about five minutes as his hoe remain froze 20 feet from where we were standing. She knew not to be in the presence of another Pimp, especially when they were in a conversation.

Goldy finally instructed her to get in the back seat. I said, "dig this Goldy, I've laced my bottom hoe to be on the lookout for your hoe."

"What do you Mean?" Goldy said looking curious.

"Cool it Pimping!" I said, "I'm not trying to knock you for the bitch, I was just telling her when she sees your game is to lace her up about the area. We don't want the bitch to cost you any money before she make you some." Goldy smile and said, "Mac Goldie, I really do appreciate your assistance and support. I'm more than grateful for the love you have shown, but I'm able to make it from here." "Okay cool baby," I said. I understood his insecureness because of the lack of loyalty Pimp's show one another. When Pimping began, is when friendships end, is the understanding a Pimp needs to know when he plays this game. But what Goldy didn't know was that I was a "True Stand-Up Guy" when it came to a friendship. Like I said though, I understood his insecureness, and I wasn't about to end our friendship over a misunderstanding.

He must have read my mind because he apologized.

"Mac Goldie forgive me if I sounded like I didn't trust you. But please understand Goldie, I've been cross by every Pimp that I've considered to be my friend. Also, I haven't had a Hoe that could stand up to my Pimping in a while."

I cut him off and said, "I understand clearly when you say that it's hard to trust anyone in this business, but dig this Pimping, this time you've met a real Blue-Ribbon Pimp. I'm your brother just as much as your friend." Goldy embraced me this time with a hug.

If no one else noticed, I'm sure his hoe peeped out the genuine love we had for one another. When we got inside the car Goldy's Hoe head was faced to the floor. So, I guess she didn't see the emotional moment Goldy, and I shared. I cracked the back windows so that Goldy's hoe wouldn't hear our conversation. I was giving him a rundown on where his hoe was going to be working.

I said, "Goldy this is a million-dollar spot that I'm turning you on to." I continued to say, "what makes this track a million dollars spot is the game a Pimp install into his hoe. If you laced her with the Thief Game, there's no limit to what the hoe might come in with. These Mexicans keep their whole life savings on them. So, if the bitch creeps a wallet, it could be the title to your next ride you going to cop." Goldy gave me a cold smile with his eyes and said, "Well Mac Goldie we will see what the hoe adds up to at the end of today." Testing to see was she listening to Goldy and I conversation Goldy said, "Dana, did you hear what I was taking about to my brother?" Showing her lying skills, she kept her head face toward the window and said, "No Daddy." She knew not to say yes.

Before we dropped Dana off, Goldy wanted to make a quick stop at K-Mart to get some condoms for Dana protection. I told Goldy to tell her to get a box of 36 condoms, the biggest box. Goldy looked at me and said, "Damn Pimping, what you trying to do, run my hoe off?" He continued to say, "Mane, I want to break the bitch not blow the hoe!" All I can do is smile and say, "The reason I said get the biggest box was because there are going to be plenty of Mexicans that want her service. And she wouldn't have to call you to bring her more condoms when the bitch can already have them with her." Goldy looked around to his hoe once again and said, "Listen Baby Pumpkin, I want you to go inside and buy the biggest box of condoms they have okay?"

"Yes Daddy." She said with devotion. "Baby there's going to be plenty of Mexicans that you can trick, steal and flat back with. That's why I want you to buy as many condoms as you can because I don't want you to miss any money. Remember baby, each condom cost forty or more. So, make sure you don't lose not one of them or have to use two of them on one trick unless he gives you more money, understand?"

"Yes Daddy." She said again. This time sounding even more confident.

When she got out the car, she immediately started running inside the store! *What the fuck is wrong with this bitch?* Before I could say anything Goldy was sitting across me smiling and said, "Oh Yea, I forgot to tell you Mac Goldie the bitch want me to help her lose weight, so I told the bitch whenever I send her to get something run and do it!" I laughed so hard holding my stomach then said, "Well I hope the people inside the store don't think the bitch stole something running to this car!" Goldy looked at me and pointed at the door and said, "Here she come running back to the car." Breathing hard and talking fast at the same time she sounded like she was giving birth to Goldy's new Cadillac Deville he wants. *Damn pimping ain't easy but somebody got to do it!* And Goldy Locs was definitely fit for the suit!!
Riding through the apartment where Dana was going to be working, I saw my hoe Jazz with a gang of Mexicans on her way to satisfy them. You would've thought

that she was a bottle of Tequila the way they was holding her. When Dana saw this, I felt the vibration of motivation running through her! She couldn't wait to show Goldy how much she was for his Pimping!! He had already pimped four hundred dollars out of her ass, and I'm sure he was going to get at least a thousand more before the night was over.

Once we dropped Goldy hoe off, we headed back downtown to exercise our game on the next bitch.
Before we could reach the expressway, Goldy received a phone call from his hoe. She was calling to see was it ok if she went with this Mexican to the hotel for $300? Goldy instructed her, "to pick the hotel, which needs to be in the same area where you working," he said. I clearly understood the reason for telling her that. It was for her protection. He didn't want the trick to take her somewhere she didn't know nothing about. Rape her, then take her money. So, a hoe needs to know, all

the instructions that a Pimp instill in his hoe is for her security.

Approaching 285 West headed downtown to the underground mall, Goldy and I wanted to see could we catch up with Slick Frank to see what type of action he had going on. We passed a store that Goldy was telling me about his personal photographer. He said, "you know Mac Goldie, when I check me a nice trap off this bitch, I want you and I to go take some pictures together to put on my "Wall of Fame." I wasn't really into taking pictures, but the relationship Goldy and I was building I wanted something to remember him by.

Chapter 15

Cruising through Five Point Underground, both sides of the sidewalk was full of all type of bitches. Black, White and Spanish bitches. I broke down the speed limit on my car to 10 mph so we wouldn't pass up our next bitch. I cracked both of my back windows an inch from being open so that traffic could hear Curtis Mayfield scream Pimping out the speakers.

Before I could park my Pimping, Goldy received a phone call again from his new hoe, letting him know that she been done from flipping the trick for the $300 and plus she stole a wallet with $742 in it. I can see the spark in Goldy eyes when he hung up the phone saying to me, "Goldie, before you park, let's go break on this bitch for the thousand dollars trap she have on her."

I said, "Goldy did she say whether or not the money was hot?" He answered back, "I wouldn't give a fuck if the money is hot or not, the hoe has too much money of mines in her possession, and to me that means, the money is hot."

I understood Goldy insecureness for wanting to get his money off her. For one, a hoe with too much money on her for the first time could cause her to make the wrong move. Also, Goldy hadn't check this kind of money out of a hoe ass in a while. Even worse than that, the cops will rob a hoe quick in that area.

In this game, you must be smarter and quicker than the cops and your hoe, because at any time she could be snatched by the cops or another fast hustler. Hoes are to be charged and broke for every dollar and valuables that she has in her possession, and only left with a Pimp's game on how to get up on some more money. Having belief is the richest value a hoe could have. Any real stomp down hoe knows she never supposed to go broke after leaving a good pimp with all the game he installed in his hoe.

I made a right turn on Piedmont St. to exit on to the expressway when Goldy cut in saying, "Damn Mac Goldie, is this as fast as this car can go?" His remark pissed me the fuck off until I had to bring him back to being a Pimp!! I said, "dig this Jack, you not going to make me turn my 'Lac' into a flying jet, just because you acting insecure with your Pimping!" He went to say something, but I cut him off and said, "if the hoe is for you, then it wouldn't matter if we waited until tomorrow to go break on the bitch. She's gonna have that trap and some more to put with it!" I toned down the volume in my voice and said, "dig this baby, you can't change the game. The only way you going to know if you pimping or not, is when you send that hoe out the door with instructions. It's on her if the bitch keep going or make it back to you. "You can't stop that." This time Goldy sounded more confident and said, "dig that Mac Goldie, Dig that. Now that's Pimping!"

Making our way off Pleasant Road in Gwinnett County, we was on the scene within 20 minutes. Goldy instructed his hoe to be in the front entrance, so when we pulled up, she can jump straight in the back seat, break herself for the thousand dollars and get back to work. As soon as she seen us, she was smiling like she had lost a hundred pounds and ready to show Goldy her appreciation.

"Hi Daddy, I made $75 more dollars while I was waiting on you. Also, I have like twenty Mexicans waiting on me to come back."

"That's cool, Baby girl," Goldy said. "How many condoms do you have left?" She answered back breathing hard, "I don't know Daddy, I think I have at least still thirty, because I only used six to get what I gave you." She took a deep breath then exhale and said, "Daddy, I remember what you told me, "these condoms are evidence and I need to get rid of them for some money." She continued saying, "I promise next time you come break me, all of them will be gone! Goldy was smiling and now full of Pimp spirit when he said, "Mac Goldie, looks like I have me a hoe baby." I shook his hand and said, "dig that Pimping."

As we pulled away from the apartments, Gwinnett Police was just pulling in. *I'm glad I have this twenty percent tint on my windows.* Soon as we left out the apartments my bottom hoe Jazz was calling, "Hello," I said.

"Daddy, didn't I just see you leaving from over here?"

"Yes, you did. Why? What's up?"

"Daddy, the game is a little slow for me right now, but I'm still down and going to make something happen."

I said, "dig that Baby girl, but what's your score?"

"Daddy, I only have $400 right now but like I said, I'm going to make something happen."

She continued to say, "oh yeah, Daddy, I seen that turnout you was telling me about. She's real frisky, but you can tell she has some instructions in her because she's only flirting with money."

"Dig that." I said, "call me once you make your thousand okay?"

"Yes Daddy, I love You!" The click on of the phone told her I love you back but not me.

Goldy was counting his trap that he just checked off his bitch. She had lied about the money she said she made. As I said earlier, "a Pimp don't believe anything a hoe says, until she placed it in his hands. He had already check his hoe for eleven hundred and eighty dollars and she was still down showing loyalty, respect, and dedication. I can see the look on his face that he was feeling more confident and motivated with his game and action.

He pulled $600 from his trap and said, "Goldie, here's what I owe you for helping me out with my rent. He continued to say, "I could never pay you back for what you put back into me, which is hope and motivation." I cut in and said, "Goldie, you already had these values in you, you just

needed to be around your kind, which was a True Bonified Pimp! You don't owe me nothing baby, just keep on Pimping!"
"Dig that baby," is what Goldy said, "Dig that!

It was time for my hoes to give me a rundown, my first phone call was from my pecan tanned pretty little hoe Melissa.
"Hi Daddy,"
"What's up pretty angel?" I said sounding more motivating than her.
"Daddy, vice is hotter than the weather over here. I only have three hundred and forty-two dollars. Will you please take me to another track so I can add up to a respectable trap?" I wasn't about to come to the bitch rescue, so I said, "Dig this pretty angel, the next trick you catch have him drop you off at the Chamblee Tucker Apartments on Chamblee Road."
"Yes Daddy, thank you." Before I could hang up the phone, I was receiving another call. This time from my young fruit Infinity.
"Hello," I answered.

"Hey Daddy!"

"What's up Baby Thief?"

"Pimping and hoeing," she answered back in a good hoe spirit. "Daddy, I don't know what Michelle have but my score is $560. I flat back for every dollar, and I haven't ran across a lick." She went to popping it saying, "Daddy, I really like working with Michelle, she's hipping me to what these Mexicans saying in Spanish. I'm finished from shaking everything down in the back of the apartment. Michelle and I have teamed up. Daddy, I promise my next phone call is going to be my lick! You'll see. Here's Michelle Daddy."

"Hi Daddy," Michelle said sounding just as happy as Infinity.

"What's up thick bunny," I joked.

"I have $475 Daddy."

"Okay cool," I said.

"Infinity told me she like working with you, you hoes better not be doing no funny bunny shit!"

"Daddy no, I will never cross you out for another hoe! I'm down for your crown

Daddy. All another bitch can do with me, is help me get you some more money." The expression on her voice was begging me to believe her.

"Damn Michelle, hoe you starting to sound like me. Doing a lot of popping it, but bitch, you know what I put my belief into, your action. So, what you need to is take all of them words and turn them into verbs."

"Okay Daddy, I will."

Making our way back downtown to the underground I agreed to go with Goldy to take some pictures. Once we made it to the underground, we both stepped out of the car catching everyone's attention. We definitely had on the colors that matched our style and personality. Some older lady that looked like she could have been close to ninety years old said, "Damn, where were you two handsome players back in 1935?" Goldy smiled and gave the homeless woman twenty dollars. Then said, "You might still have a couple more miles left in you, because you sure know what to say."

We walked in the department where Goldy's photo friend worked. She looked like an ex-hooker back in her days. Her eyes lit up with fascination and infatuation when she seen Goldy and I. Her smile spoke before her mind saying, "Oh My God! Who is this Goldy?"
"Oh, this my twin brother Mac Goldie. She continued to flirt saying, "I don't know Goldy, I think he looks a little better than you." I cut her off before she could say anything else and said, "your name got to be Suzy." She started smiling and blushing then said, "no, my name isn't Suzy but I'm choosing if your fee's affordable." I took her by the hands and brought her close to me then said, "Oh Baby, all I need from you is one million in cash and a trip to the moon with a Star like you." She looked over at Goldy. This time blushing harder than before. Then said to him, "He's charisma." Goldy cut her off and said, "No! He's

more than just charisma, he's a blessing!"

This time taking my pimping a lot more serious than before she said, "well Goldie, I believe I'm a little bit too old and self-independent to choose a Pimp, but I would love to take some pictures of you for free."

"Okay, you win Mrs.…, Damn forgive me, I never got your name?" She smiled with them pretty blue eyes and said, "call me Peggie."

I said, "well okay Peggie, what's it going to be baby? I want more than some free pictures." Before I can say another word Goldy cut me off and saved the old ex-hooker. He switched the subject and said, "Dig this Mac Goldie, she has all different sizes you can order your pictures in." I peeped what he was doing so I change the subject as well and said, "How bout we get them in all sizes!!" We took over thirty memorable pictures and built some valuable time the whole day.

At the end of the night Goldy had checked $1900 out his hoe ass. He tried more than twice to give me back what I gave him, but I wouldn't accept it. My trap that night added up to $5,285. *What a respectable trap,* I thought to myself Goldy and I made tonight. We both agreed to meet the next day for lunch. After I dropped my game off at the apartment, I jump back in traffic to see what Greyhound had to offer.

Chapter 16

I spotted at 2:30am, a bitch standing in front of the bus station by herself. She looked like a square bitch out of college mix with a little hoe in her. She stood at least 5'7" flat, in her icy white k-swiss tennis shoes with a tennis shirt outfit on. I know she wasn't ready for the business I was about to bring to her, so I parked in a close spot to observe her next move. Just as I thought, she was a square looking for a nut.

For an occasion like this, I kept me a changing outfit in the trunk of the car. I switched into a dope boy outfit. I knew if I would have presented myself to a square in my Pimp uniform, it would either intimidate her or she would have the wrong understanding about a Pimp. So, I had to put on an outfit that would at least hold her up for a minute so that she will listen.

I changed faster than Superman but without his cape. When she saw me get out of my Pimp mobile, she immediately put on her defensive guards. But my offensive plays were too smooth for her to stop.

"Excuse Me," I said, "how long have you been standing here pretty?" She blushed and said, "I don't know, I'll say about twenty minutes, why?"

"Did you by chance see an older lady waiting here?"

"No," she said. Sounding very helpful. "No one has been standing here but me for the last ten minutes. You sure she hasn't already left? Because, I did see an older black woman get inside of a taxi before you pulled up." I continued to pop it and said, "No, my mother wouldn't have took a taxi when she knew I was on my way to get her."

"Sorry, I forgot to introduce myself. I'm Mac Goldie, what's your name?"

"Sara," she said in a soft tone. "Why do they call you Mac Goldie? Are you some type of player or something?"

I laughed to myself and said, "No Sara, I've been graduated from playing games. Now I'm a man of understanding." She looked at me from head to toe then asked, "How old are you Mac Goldie?"
I said discreetly, "Baby, I'm an old mind inside of a young body. But the only baby that I have in me are my dreams." I continued macking and said, "I believe that I can do anything through God and my belief." My spiritual technique immediately captivated her interest into asking me, "So Goldie, tell me, do you have a girlfriend?"
"Sure I do! I have lots of girlfriends, but I'm not in no relationship, marriage or anything."
"Come on now," she said, hoping I was telling her the truth. "Good as you look, you telling me you don't have a girlfriend?" I look into her eyes and said, "No, I'm serious pretty I do not have a lady! That's by choice not force that I'm not involved in a relationship. Really you can say, I'm more into relations than I am

in relationships. That way, no one will be feeling pressure or obligated."
She said, "I like that Mac Goldie, but I still think you have a girlfriend?"
I flirted back like she was doing and said, "I like the way you say Mac Goldie. What about you Sara? Are you involved in a relationship?" She dropped her head looking, not sure what she has and said, "Yes, I guess you can say I'm in a relationship, but it's not that serious."
"I can tell," I said. Her eyes looked at me with a question mark then she said, "How can you tell Mr. Psychic?" I came a little closer to her and said, "Because, what man in his right mind would let his woman ride greyhound without any proper instruction all by herself? By the way, where are you on your way to?" She looked as if she wanted to cry and said, "You're right, I'm all alone. I'm headed to Louisville, Kentucky."
"Is that where you're from I asked?"
"Yes, I am Goldie." I put my hand on top of my head and said, "Then tell me this

Sara, where are you coming from?" Still looking sad she said, "Well actually you can say I'm leaving. I've been here in Atlanta for two months with my boyfriend, until he put his hands on me because he thinks I'm cheating on him. I asked her out of curiosity, "What did you do for him to think that?"

"NOTHING!" She said with a smiling lie. "Okay, whatever baby," I said. "So, tell me, what time does your bus leave?" I asked to see do I have enough time to steal her. She reached inside her purse look at her ticket and said impatiently, "Six O'clock a.m."

"Well Sara, I have to be honest. I'm not going to be able to stand here until six o'clock talking to you. Would you like to sit in my car so that both of us will be comfortable and get an understanding?" She smiled sinfully and said, "What kind of understanding are you talking about?" I said, "Understanding about your past relationship and your future relation with me." She smiled and said, "Who said anything about having a relation with you?"

"No one had to say anything Pretty, you already done gave me thirty minutes of your time. I'm sure another thirty minutes won't hurt. How about you get inside and let's take a ride to see whether or not you want to still leave or stay? I promise to bring you back whenever you ready." She hesitated for a second then said, "You better not try anything Mac Goldie!" I said back smiling, "I won't, just as long as you don't try to do something to me first!"

She placed her bags in the back seat still looking undecided. I made her feel more comfortable when I ask her, "Do you have family, friends or anyone that you're in contact with."

"No," she said. My mother is somewhere on drugs and I fucking hate my father. Far as family, I have no one Goldie. Oh, I'm sorry. I mean Mac Goldie." I knew now was the time for me to lay down my macking and bring her into my world.

"So, tell me Sara, you promise to be honest with me about everything that I ask you?"

"Yes," she said in a joking way. "No Sara, I'm serious! You must know in order for us to grow in this relation we have to communicate. If you rather go first asking me questions, feel free to ask me anything you want."

She said, "Okay cool! What do you do for a living Mr. Mac Goldie?" I knew the word pimping would have spooked her, so I use that I'm a *"Motivational Consultant"* also a mentor and spiritual adviser." She smiled as if I was joking until she seen the cold look on my face. Then she said sounding serious this time, "Are you serious?"

"Of course, I am! Now it's time you start taking me serious and be straight up with me." She looked a little spook and said, "Okay Sorry, I didn't mean to upset you. Maybe you should drop me back off at Greyhound." Not sounding thirsty at all I said, "That's on you Sara, if you want me to take you back, but if you do leave, you might miss out on your calling."

"What is my calling Goldie? Sorry, Mac Goldie?"

"You never know Sara, maybe you might become the next star in my life."

She froze for a second then said, "You sound like a PIMP! Are you?" I asked her back, "Are you a Hoe?"

"Hell Nah," she shouted! "Let me out this damn car!" I had to cool her down before telling her, "Dig this Sara, I didn't get offended when you called me a pimp, did I? Then why did you get offended when I asked were you a hoe?" She said, "I don't know. I guess it made me think of when my father would beat and molest me. He'll always say, you're going to grow up and be just like your mother, a Hooker."

She said with tears in eyes, "Believe it or not Goldie his mental abuse hurt more than the physical abuse." She started to do everything a turn-out do in an interview, which is start crying. This was nothing new to me. Out of all the girls I done interviewed, 90 percent of them have been mentally, physically, or emotional abused.

I gave her my "Pimp Support" and wrapped my concerned arms around her. She cuddled up in my arms and continued giving me what I wanted to hear. She said, "Mac Goldie, I really don't want to go back home because there's really nothing there for me to do. I'm scared to stay here in Atlanta because it's too violent. It's like I want to leave but I don't. Does that make any sense to you Goldie?"

"Sure, it does pretty. But you have to understand something Sara, when you're caught up in a situation like yours and a blessing come your way, you have to be able to recognize it." I continued macking to her while she laid her damp face on my chest. I said, "You might don't believe what I'm about to tell you Sara, but dig this, I was chilling at my house about to lay down when something told me to ride through Greyhound." She jumped from under my arms and shouted, "I thought you came here to get your mother!" I gently grabbed her hand and said, "Pretty, when I seen you, I had to think of a magnificent lie to get your time. You had two looks on your face. One that said you was going through something, and the other one you wanted to tell someone. So, I had to ask you something that would make you feel comfortable to talk." She smiled and said, "Damn, you smooth!" My smile agreed to what she said.

"So now that I have your time and attention Sara, I promise anything you ask me and what I tell you will be the truth okay?" She looked at me with them sky blue eyes and said, "You are a Pimp, aren't you?"

"Baby I done already told you what I am, so why are you stuck on this Pimp question?" I test her and said, "If I told you that I was, will you believe me?"

"YES!" she said quickly!

"What if I told you no, would you believe that also?"

"NO!" she said this time with a look on her face hoping I wasn't.

"Sara answer this, have you ever been with a Pimp?"

"NO! And I don't plan on being with one."

"Why?" I asked. "You must have heard some bad things about a Pimp?"

"Yes," she said. "My cousin was with one, and all he ever did was beat her and take her money." I asked Sara out of curiosity, "What did she do to get beat?"

"NOTHING!" she said angrily!

"Well Sara all I can tell you is that all Pimps are not the same. You have Gorilla Pimps, Slick Pimps and Pimps that have finesse." She shouted as if she won a prize, "That's You, The finesse Pimp!" All I could do is smile and said, "Okay, you win Sara. Yes, I am a PIMP. I want to be your Pimp and you my hoe. I want to be your family, your best friend and most of all the remedy to all your problems. I want to be your motivation when you feeling low, the one you feel comfortable to tell your discreteful secrets to. Also, Sara, you must need me just as much as I want you." She sprinkled my chest with tears and said, "Mac Goldie, I do need you "BAD! But Goldie, I never been with a Pimp before." I rubbed my fingers through her hair and said, "That's a lie Baby, you with a Pimp right now. Tell me how does it feel?" She cuddled more into my arms and said, "IT FEELS GREAT! Please don't let me go Goldie!" Instead of me bringing her closer to me, I braced my arms in her chest and pushed her 3 inches away from me so that I could look her in the eyes and said, "Baby as bad as I want to hold and caress you in your deepest inner emotions, I can't. I must know not only do you want to be with me but also for me as well. I want you to dedicate your mind, body and soul to me." Her body was shaking when she said, "I don't know Goldie, maybe this is a little too fast for me. What do you think?"

"Baby it's not what I think it's what I already know. And yes, I do think you qualify for the business, just as long as you know how to follow instructions. But if you don't, not only could you get hurt by someone, even worst you could lose your life. That's why you must pay attention to every word that I say. My instructions are your security. It will protect you from killers, hoe stealers and drug dealers." I continued lacing her up with the game. Then I said, "in order for us to grow we must have an understanding." She cut in and said, "I thought we do have an understanding? I want to be with you and for you Mac Goldie," she said.

"Are you sure I asked her?"

"YES, I really do!"

"Well baby the way to get this game started you have to turn everything over to me. This mean money, jewelry or any other values you have put away."

She said, "Well Mr. Goldie I don't have nothing but a hundred and probably twenty dollars, do you want that?"

"That's a start on the first million we are about to make," I said. She grabbed my hand and said, "Mr. Goldie may I ask you a question?"

"Sure pretty, speak on it."

She said, "Do you have any more girls?"

"Why Pretty? Do you need help to support us?"

"No, I just was asking because it would be nice to have someone to work with."

"Well Sara, one thing you should know and that is, I'm the only Pimp you know. So, if you happen to run into anyone talking about anything other than the business be sure to get out their presence immediately! I don't want you to converse with nothing but money. The only pleasure you going to get out of this is making money and when we're together. Listen Sara, there's going to be some hot days, cold nights and rainy mornings, through it all you must stay focused and loyal. You asked me how many girls do I have? Well, if you qualify, you will make my sixth girl." I had her full attention as I continue to stroke her with my charm. "Sara, in this game dreams come true. You are going to be the one that make these dreams come true. In the meantime, baby you got to keep that belief in me and yourself. I'm going to introduce you to someone you will be working with. Her name is Jazz. She's pretty like you and beautiful like me. What makes Jazz so beautiful is the properness that I instilled in her." I asked her, "Do you Understand?" To see was she paying attention to me, "Yes I Do." She reached inside her purse and gave me the $120 along with her I.D.

She looked me in my eyes and said, "Goldie, are you sure I'm going to be okay?"

"Baby, you're going to be more than okay. At times you're going to think you're lucky but really your blessed." She smiled with them pretty white teeth and said, "I already feel like I'm blessed." I thought to myself, "This pretty little hoe already have some game about herself." Once Sara gave me the money, we exited the curve into the moving traffic, talking about the game and the rules.

She didn't fully understand the game, but she wasn't naive as you think. She studied every move that I made and every word that came out my mouth. She was looking at me as if she was in a trance. Her eyes ran laps around my body. I thought to myself, she's too fresh to bring home, maybe I should get her a room, so that I can finish lacing her up.

When I exit off the expressway there was a Best Western Hotel. When we pulled into the parking lot, I read her thoughts and I knew what she was thinking. I sent her on the inside to cop a room. She got out the car smiling looked back at me and put an extra twist on her switch. I stayed calm and said to myself, *I'm going to teach her to sell that same game in the streets.*

Chapter 17

She came back within 10 minutes and said, "We're on the 10th floor. Room 1017." I was very familiar with this room because this is where I set up my girls to play conventions when they are in town. Downstairs next to the lobby was a bar where potential tricks hung out. In the same parking lot was an I-Hop restaurant that was always full of executive businessmen that would love to have Sara for lunch. 1017 was the room Jazz would always request, because on the balcony you can see downtown Atlanta. It was the prefect set up to interview a hoe for the streets!

Sara looked at me as if she was upset. I guess because she carried all her luggage up to the room. She figured since I talk like a gentleman that I was supposed to get her bags. What she didn't know was the only heavy thing that I ever carried was a pocket full of money.

Once Sara finish from unpacking her clothes she asked me, "Goldie, do you want to join me in the shower?"
"No Pretty, you go head and get yourself together so that I can finish giving you some game on how I want you to work." When she stepped into the shower, I burglarized her luggage looking for any hidden values she might have tried to hide.

Inside her suitcase were pictures of her family and ex- boyfriend. He looked like the singer Ginuwine. I thought to myself, if I was into pimping boys, I would have put him in the game as a gigolo. I laughed to myself at the crazy thought that ran through my head. As I was rolling me a blunt, Sara came out the shower with nothing on but the hair on her head. She looked like Brittney Spears with a fatter ass. She said, "Goldie, will you pass me my lotion and put some on my back?"
I knew that she was trying to be a temptation in the game, so I had to show her that my self-discipline was more

powerful than her body.

"Sure," I said. "Bring me the lotion and also your body. Lay flat on your stomach." Instead of her laying flat, she arched her back into a fuck position. I said, "DAMN Sara! Do you want me to put the lotion on your back or on your ass?" She giggled and said, "I want you to put it in my ass." I immediately stopped her from trying to seduce me and said, "Listen Baby, save that freak shit for the streets! It's too early in this relation for us to be fucking around. I want you to focus and stay strong in the head. You understand?"
"Yes, I do Mac Goldie, I'm sorry. I feel so embarrassed for acting this way in front of you." Sara never had a man to turn her body down and go strictly for her soul.

Not only did I caress her body with lotion, but I gave her a dose of my "Pimp Devotion." Her body was smooth as a seal, with a pecan tan, that looked like she stole from *Baywatch.* You can tell that she only been with a few guys by the low mileage I peeped on her cunt. Sara looked up at me still not believing how self-discipled I was. She rolled over on her back and said, "Goldie I never met someone like you. You're unbelievable, and definitely a man I can respect!" I said, "Speaking of respect Sara, that's what I want from you before you give me any money. Understand?"

"Yes Daddy, I mean Goldie." She said as if she made a mistake.

"See there," I said, "You already calling me your Daddy. Dig this though Sara, I want you to put on your best eye-catching outfit and get ready to show me your dedication." Still trying to flirt with me she said, "But Daddy, I already have on my best outfit, my Birthday Suit." I gave her a cold smile so that she would start taking me serious, then I said, "Your Birthday Suit isn't legal baby to walk the streets. Now reach in your suitcase and bring an outfit. One of them outfits that makes you look a piece from being

naked." She said, "The only thing I have like that are my sleeping clothes."
"Let me see them because we just might turn them into your working clothes," I said." She smiled and brought out a pajama set that looked like a G-Sting with a half T-Shirt that read *Bad Girls.*

It was close to six o'clock, which was perfect timing for her to catch some tricks in the hotel lobby. I instructed her to go order some breakfast for herself and also to be on the lookout for a trick.
"Sara, there's a heavy-set white guy who is the security in the lobby that I want you to get an understanding with. He sometimes spend money with the girls and then plays security for them."

After giving Sara a thirty-minute rundown on the area she was going to be working, she was ready to show me what I instructed her to do. "Sara, it's 6 o'clock now, and I want you to check in with me around 1 this afternoon when lunch hours are over. I don't want you to go anywhere working other than this hotel and the parking lot." I didn't want to take her to the fast track yet until I made sure she knew how to follow instructions. It would have been an immature pimp move to put her around some veteran hookers and hoe stealing pimps, knowing she was still a virgin to the game. When working the fast track, a hoe must be laced from head to toe on how to carry herself.

I left Sara at the hotel, then made my way to the girls apartment. I wanted to hip them all to their new "Wifey." When I opened the door my youngest hoe Infinity was up watching this movie called, *The Temptation.*

"Damn Lil' Baby, it's ten minutes after seven. What you doing up so early?"

"Ready to go to work," she said in a freakish tone. I knew it was me who she wanted to go to work on, but I went along with her lie and said, "well get dress then, I have some fresh game that I want you to work with." She said disappointed, "Daddy, where do you want me to work? I mean, what type of outfit should I put on?"

"Bitch I don't know! Look in your closet and grab two of them tennis shirt outfits for you and Sara. I'm sure she can fit your size clothes and shoes. You and Sara are going to play on Cleveland and Steward Ave today. Infinity I want you to teach Sara how to hoe in all aspects, Flat Backing, Stealing, and how to sell Conversation."

"Yes Daddy." She said then asked, "Daddy, is she white or black?"

"She's white bitch! Does it matter?" I continued to roast her and said, "I wouldn't give a fuck if she was black, white, or a motherfucking zebra stripe, she a "HOE" in my eyes!" Infinity broke down crying like she always do and said, "I'm sorry Daddy, I didn't mean to upset you. I just know you rather have a snow over a crow."

I grabbed Infinity by the head and pulled her closer to me and said, "Listen to me hoe and I mean you listen good. Stop counting yourself out and start putting more belief in yourself. Once a hoe chooses me it wouldn't matter what color she was. She's Goldie's Hoe now!

She's going to be a beautiful reflection of me. Just like You. You a black hoe, right?"

"Yes Daddy," she said smiling. But look how you turned out to be, "beautiful just like me." Infinity took my hand and balled it up into a fist, then kiss it and said, "Daddy thank you for turning me into a beautiful hoe." Within twenty minutes, Infinity was dressed in her Serena Williams tennis shirt outfit. To me, she looked more beautiful than Serena Williams. It was because she was laced with my Pimping.

Chapter 18

I haven't had any sleep in over sixteen hours, and I was more tired than a Hebrew slave. But it was something about Pimping that gave me that extra strength and motivation.

Diving back into the morning traffic, Infinity and I cruised the streets on our way to work like every other businessperson in the morning. Breaking the silence I asked Infinity, "Hey Baby, do you want to grab a steak and biscuit sandwich from Mrs. Winners?"

"Yes Daddy, but I would rather taste you for breakfast Daddy. That way I will be good and full!" I smiled and said, "You ain't nothing but an eight o'clock in the morning freak. Remember this though baby freak. I'm a Hoe's dinner not breakfast. So, if you have a good day, then later you might be able to feel and taste Daddy. Okay?"

"Ok Daddy," she said with a look on her face like she didn't believe me.

After leaving Mrs. Winners on Steward Ave, we were three minutes from where Sara was working. When we pulled into the hotel Infinity spotted Sara with her jealous eyes. Sara was talking to a trick with one hand on his wallet and the other one in his pocket. Infinity shook Sara down from head to toe then said, "Daddy, look at this out-of-pocket white bitch working in my spot!"

"Damn Infinity, you must be looking at the wrong bitch! Cause the bitch I'm looking at is in pocket as long as she's for my Pimping. That's the turnout that you going to be working with today." She grumped, "OH!"

Sara and the trick must have got an understanding because they both was headed up to Sara's room. I waited a cool fifteen minutes and saw the trick come out of Sara's room with a look on his face like he was satisfied. Once he left the scene Infinity and I went up to the Sara's room, so she can meet her new in-law.

Before we could make it to the room Sara caught another trick in the hotel lobby. *Damn this young bitch body is a bait to catch fishes.*

In less than thirty minutes she had flipped two tricks and was shaking down the lobby for more. This time when she came off the elevator, she saw me and Infinity in the lobby. When she seen me, her smile confirmed that she had a nice trap for me. She shouted excited, "Hi Daddy, I'm so glad to see you! I have something for you." She read my eyes to wait until we were inside the room to give me my money. I introduced them, "Sara this is Infinity, one of your sisters that you will be working with today." Sara reached her hand out with a smile and said, "Hi Infinity."

"Hello Sara! Daddy told me you was pretty, but he didn't say you was fine too." Infinity said making Sara feel welcome. They embraced one another with a hug as we got on the elevator and went up to Sara's room.

Once we were inside the room Sara immediately went and lifted the bed mattress where she hid my trap. She put the money in order like I instructed her to do then placed it in my hand. Screaming my business out loud Sara said, "Daddy, I only caught four tricks. Each one gave me a hundred and fifty dollars. No, I'm sorry! One gave me a hundred, and I spent five dollars to buy some more condoms. If you guys will excuse me, I need to take me a shower. That last trick was nasty!"

"Go 'head and excuse yourself Sara," I said. "Infinity, go to the car and bring that outfit up for Sara. By the way, what size shoes you wear Sara?" Feeling like she was now part of the family she smiled and said, "size six and a half Daddy." Infinity made it to the car and back within 15 seconds. I can tell she ran there and back the way she was breathing like she had done hit a lick! But the real reason she ran was because she didn't want to leave me with Sara alone. This hoe feelings for me was more than love, IT WAS POSSESSIVE, which was the wrong emotion to have in this game. I said to Infinity, "Listen hoe, them square feelings you have for me is going to end up separating us. I continued to remind her, "Bitch, you know how this relation started! And that's the same way it's going to end! Do you understand me Hoe?"

"Yes Daddy, I'm sorry!"

"Bitch, stop being sorry and get focused," I said. "Okay Daddy, I won't say I'm sorry anymore. But will you please forgive me and let me make it up to you?"

"YOU WILL BITCH! Now go help your sister get ready for work."

It was close to eleven o'clock when Infinity and Sara finished getting ready. Prefect timing! It was lunch hours. They both looked like two Athletic Hookers. The splitting image of Serena Williams and Lindsay Davenport. I instructed them to work together so that Infinity could show Sara some moves.

As we was headed to the car, the security guard recognized Infinity and told her with his freak smile that he wanted to see her later. Infinity peeped his freak signal and smiled back in agreement. Once I dropped them off on Steward Ave, it was close to 12 o'clock p.m. I thought to myself, *no way I'm going to be able to stay up and have lunch with Goldy today. I was too tired to drive myself home.*

When I pulled up to the apartment, I can tell the girls was up. I seen Melissa peeping out of the curtains as if she was waiting on my arrival. When I entered the house, there was three ass kissing smiles greeting me with pleasure and respect. "Good morning Daddy," they all spoke at the same time as if they were Charlie's Angels.

"What's up babies," I spoke back. Michelle continued to speak saying, "Daddy, none of us have seen Infinity this morning. She's not in her room!"

"She's not," I cut in before she could say another word and said, "Michelle, how many times do I have to tell you to worry about me and your own ass?"

"I'm sorry Daddy, I guess you can say that I was more concerned than worried."

"Baby its cool to have love and concern for your In-law, but if you happen to wake up one morning and everyone has left me except you, then you need to be grateful that you still have me. Hoes choose Pimps, not hoes!!"

Already in my ashtray was an afternoon blunt. I told Jazz to fire it up and meet me in the back room. "Daddy, may Melissa and I go cop us something to eat," Michelle asked?"

"Sure Baby."

"Do you want anything Daddy?"

"No baby, I'm cool."

"What about you Jazz," Michelle asked?

"It depends, where are you guys going to get something to eat?"

"I don't know, maybe Taco Bell."

"That's cool, bring me back whatever you get Michelle," Jazz said. Before Michelle went out the door, I reminded her to bring back some cigars. Melissa gave me a counterfeit smile that showed me she was becoming jealous of Jazz.

Over my years of Pimping, I was able to tell when a hoe devotion had turned into square emotions. Her eyes smiled in a different way. Passing me the blunt Jazz asked, "Daddy, can I taste you?"
"Not now Jazz. I want to rundown to you how to handle my business today. I want you to take the car and drive yourself to work today. Before you go to work, I want you to ride down Steward Ave and check on this new hoe that I put down with Infinity this morning. You don't have to get out the car, just make sure you let them see my presence by riding through. Once you put yourself down be sure to put your code in my pager so that I know you are at work. If anything should happen that you need to contact me, call the house, I will be here all day."
Jazz cut in and asked, "Daddy, should I still call you every three hours or just when I make $1000?"

"Every three hours hoe!" I said.

"Okay Daddy, I can tell you sleepy. Get yourself some pimp rest."

I responded back, "I will hoe just as soon as you leave."

"Daddy, do you care if I lay beside you before I leave?" I knew that she wanted to still give me some chewing, so I let her put me to sleep with them soft pillow lips.

Chapter 19

When I woke up it was 8:27 pm, and my pager was blowing up from unanswered calls. On my phone I had twenty missed calls from Infinity, Jazz, Michelle, Melissa and Goldy Locs. The first unanswered call that I made was to Goldy. He answered the phone sounding more concern than motivated, "Mac Goldie, you ok baby? I've been calling you since one o'clock this afternoon. You had me worried baby! Are you sure you ok?"
"I appreciate your concern Goldy and forgive me for my absence, but I been unconscious sleeping since this afternoon. When I dropped you off last night I slid through Greyhound and came up on a 2:30 a.m. hoe. I finally came in and got me some sleep. But where are you now?" I asked Goldy.
"I'm down at the underground mall," Goldy said. "I have already put my hoe down in Mexican Land. She been at work

since 12 this afternoon, and already done made $600!"

"Dig That," I said, "Dig that." He continued telling me, "Oh yeah, she still have a gang of Mexicans wanting to see her. Mac Goldie I'm riding with a young friend of mine that says he know you through a bitch name Tish. His name is Lil' Tae. Do you know him?"

"Yeah, mane I know Lil' Tae! He's a true Pimp friend that is fascinated with the game. He doesn't have a Pimp bone in his body but has a heart that's bigger than this world. Put him on the phone Pimping."

"Hello, what's going on Mac Goldie," Lil' Tae asked?

"Some more Pimping," I answered! I continue to say, "I see you riding around with a Boss Player!"

He answered, "Yeah, I been knew Goldy Locs for a while. It's an honor to be in the presence of an M.V.P. Player. I might steal a little game from him," he joked.

I told Lil' Tae, "even if you were to get some game it wouldn't work for you young blood. Pimping is an art that you must have in you to do." I gave him advice to stick with what you do, which was sell dope. "Lil' Tae do me a favor?"

"Anything for you Mac Goldie! What?"

"Don't have none of that poison shit around my pimp partner."

"OH NO Mac Goldie. I will never disrespect the game like that!"

"Dig that Young Blood, Dig that! Put Goldy back on the phone."

"Yeah Pimping, I'm back on the line. What's up with you?"

"Dig this Goldy, I'm still home without transportation right now, but as soon as I call my game to bring me the car, I will give you a call okay?"

"That's cool Goldie. I'm going to have Lil' Tae stick with me until I hear from you."

"Dig That!" as we both hung up the phone.

The next call that I made was to Infinity. Her answering machine picked up on the first ring as if her phone was dead. So, I called the next un-answered call which was Jazz.

"Hello,"

"Hi Daddy, can I call you right back, I'm busy." Before I could call Melissa, Infinity was calling me back.

"Hey Daddy, I was busy when you called. So far, it's been a good day, Sara has close to a thousand. She's been catching tricks back-to-back. As a matter of fact, she's with one right now. Daddy I told her to let me hold her trap until she finishes, and she act like I was going to run off with it talking about, "you told her to hold her own trap." Infinity was upset with Sara because she was following my instructions. She didn't know that I had instructed Sara to keep her own money. I said, "Dig this Infinity, I want you to call me once Sara finishes up with that trick. Before I could hang up the phone, Infinity said, "Daddy, can I get me something to eat?"

"Sure, you can baby! Don't forget to get your sister something to eat also."

"Here she is now Daddy, you want to talk to her?"

"Yes, pass her the phone."

"Hello," a soft voice said on the phone. "Damn Lil' Pretty, you don't sound excited for the one who's been getting all the action." She said back in a demotivated spirit, "I'm tired and plus I don't like working with Infinity, she's too jealous. She's been mean mugging me Daddy ever since I told her you told me to hold my own trap. She also been asking questions about you and me. I told her that I was going to report everything she said to you and she really start acting shitty."

" Where is she now," I asked?

"Right here in my face Daddy mean mugging me."

I cut in and said, "enough about her, you stay focused okay?"

"I'm trying Daddy! I mean I'm really trying!"

"Go with Infinity to get you something to eat and wait there until I show up. Oh yeah, put her ass on the phone!"

Before I could say anything, Infinity started talking trying to justify her being out of pocket. She said screaming through the phone, "Daddy, this bitch lying on me! All I did was ask to hold her trap and she start getting smart and shit!"

"First of all," I said, "BITCH SHUT UP! I don't want to hear shit you have to say! I told you about them square ass feelings, and now you letting the next bitch peep them! Soon as you two finish eating call me!"

On the other end of the phone was Jazz calling back, "What's up Daddy?"

"What's going on Jazz?" I asked?

"I was busy when you call but I'm close to my thousand, I still have five more condoms to go. Can I call you back? once I finish up?"

"Sure, go 'head, I was just checking on you and answering all my missed calls."

"Thank you, Daddy, for checking on me," Jazz said before she hung up. Still a little frustrated with Infinity I start thinking to myself, *Damn, I wonder how long this bitch is going to last!* Infinity has a complication with white hoes. She always put herself in competition with them. She felt like tricks would choose white skin over black skin, and that a white whore could make more than a black whore in the game. But what she didn't know until later was, any whore could come up with a decent trap once Pimping put the game in her or bring it out of her.

The next call I received snap me back to reality. It was Michelle crying on the other end hysterical saying, "DADDY! I JUST GOT RAPED!!!"

"WHAT?" I said, as I told her to calm down so that I could understand her. She lowered the tone in her voice then said, "I've been Raped!"

"Damn Michelle, how that happen? What I mean is, how in the fuck did you get raped?"

Stuttering when she talked Michelle said, "Daddy, all I know is when I finished up with the trick, he pulled out a long knife and told me to give him back his money with some more sex! I tried to beg him to stop but he kept the knife to my throat saying, "Bitch! don't make me kill you!"

"Daddy, I'm so scared right now!"

"Okay cool down for a minute Michelle and answer this, did he get my money?"

She screamed through the phone, "WHAT DID YOU SAY?"

"I SAID BITCH, did he get my money?"

"That's all you care about Daddy," she asked?

"BITCH! That's what I asked about didn't I?" She barely whispered out, "NO, I still have your money."

"Okay, cool bitch, well you didn't get raped. Rape means to me they took everything. Now tell me the truth bitch! What happened?" She hesitated for a cool five second then said, "Daddy, what do you mean? You don't believe me?"

"Bitch don't ask me any questions

without answering mines. Now, I'm going to ask you one more time. WHAT HAPPENED?" This time she broke down through the phone and said, "Nothing happened Daddy. I'm sorry for lying. Today has been a bad day for me. I only have $400, and plus my period done came on."

"Listen to me bitch, if you ever lie to me again, especially about something like this I'm going to cut that lying tongue out your mouth and burn your faggot ass up, YOU HEAR ME!"

"I'm sorry Daddy," she said again trying to apologize to me more than twice.

I knew Michelle was telling me a lie when she said the rapist didn't get the money. I always taught the girls to hide my money in a safe place which was in her cunt. Now how in the fuck did she get raped, and the money was in the same spot he supposed to have took her pussy? If you not on top of your game in this business, hoes will try to run a circle around you. She will see how long you will go for her bullshit, then once you start to straighten it out, that's when she will leave and remind you how she ran game on you.

I hung up on Michelle as she was still trying to apologize to me, calling right back, I answered the phone screaming "BITCH, when I hang this phone up don't you ever call me right back like a square! Wait until later to talk with me and continue to handle my business! YOU UNDERSTAND ME?"

"Yes Daddy," she said in an ass kissing voice.

I received another phone call, this time from Melissa.

"HEY DADDY!"

"What's happening Melissa?" I said in a demotivating spirit.

"Did I do something wrong?" she asked.

"No baby girl, you cool. What's going on with you though?"

"Daddy so far tonight has been good. I have $875 and six condoms left. Do you want me to take a taxi home or wait on you?"

"Take a taxi Melissa, I have some other business to see about okay?"

"Okay," she said sounding disappointed. I haven't spent any one-on-one time with Melissa in a while. I knew she wanted bad to be with me tonight, that's why she spoke about her trap being right. And when I say, she wanted to be with me doesn't always mean sexually. She wanted me to fill her spirit and soul up with my presence. To a Hoe. The best feeling in the world is to give her Pimp a nice trap and be able to enjoy it with him. Then again, you can give a hoe 100 percent of your Pimping, by teaching her the game from A-Z, and the ungrateful bitch will still say, you haven't did shit for her. *This is definitely a "Spirit Game."* Something the soul must feel! The minute the soul doesn't feel the spirit, nothing you can do or give that hoe to make her satisfied.

Once I finished calling all of the girls, I jumped in the shower to wash off my yesterday's scent. Just when I was about to turn on the shower, Jazz was calling. "Hello."

"Hi Daddy!"

"What's up Jazz?"

"A whole lot of money," she answered. "Daddy, I made close to two thousand dollars tonight. I crept seven hundred out of this Mexican glove compartment. Do you want me to bring you the car and this money?"

"Yes Jazz," I said. "Also stop and pick up Infinity and Sara from Mrs. Winners."

Chapter 20

It was close to 10 o'clock when all of the girls finally made it to the apartment, "Everyone except Michelle. I made her stay down until she came up with a decent trap for the lie she told me earlier. When I came in the living room all the girls was talking to Sara as if she been with us for years. I cut into their conversation and said, "I see you all have met your new wife in law."

"Yes Daddy," Melissa answered, and she's cool too!"

"Daddy, can I work with Sara next time you put us down?"

"Slow down Bitch," I said. "Don't get too friendly. Let's give Sara a chance in the game first before you go trying to win her friendship. She only been here for a day, and so far, her day came with progress." I can feel Infinity eyes rolling behind my back as she acted like something was in her throat when I was commenting Sara. "Say bitch, do you have something you want to motherfucking say? Yeah, You Infinity! While you over there clearing your throat." She struck back with a quick lie, "Daddy, something was in my throat." "Mane you always getting on me Daddy!" She stumbled into her room.

"BITCH! Get your ass back out here and find you a spot." Find her a spot meant to get somewhere, sit down and don't get back up! Sara was paying attention to how I Pimp on a bitch when she's out of pocket. Instead of the scene scaring her, it gave her more respect for me.

"Jazz, have you met Sara yet?" I asked. "Yes Daddy, I think she's adorable!" Everyone embraced Sara with welcoming hugs and love. She felt no jealousy, hate, or animosity. Only joy, support, and care.

I went into my bedroom and notice on my phone that I had three missed calls. They all was from Michelle. Right when I was about to call her, she was calling back, "Hello," I said.

"Daddy, where are you? I'm sorry I didn't mean to ask that. Can you come get me please? I just stole this Mexican wallet with four thousand in it! I'm hiding in the garbage can right behind the McDonalds on Buford Hwy. I knew exactly what garbage can she was talking about. I grabbed my keys and told Sara to ride with me, so she could see how my hoes get all the way down for me.

"Oh yeah, Jazz go in Michelle room and give me a changing outfit for her."

"What kind of outfit Daddy?" Jazz asked.

"A square outfit," I said.

On the way to Michelle, Melissa wanted to know why she couldn't ride in the front seat? "Well Baby girl, let me give you some understanding about how we sit in this car. Really no one sit in the front unless you are a stranger. I have all of my girls to sit behind me in the order each one of you came in. Like you for instance, you my fifth girl. Which means you will sit right behind me, all the way to the left. To your right will be Melissa, then Michelle, Infinity and all the way to the right will be Jazz.

"Oh" she said, "I'll be glad when I can move all the way to the right where Jazz is." I peeped the game she threw in the air for me to catch and said, "Baby girl, be happy with the spot you already have in my life, and that's being with me. Positions are not easy to get with me. EVERYTHING IS EARNED, and it doesn't happen for you over night!" I brought you with me so you can see how down and loyal my girls are for my Pimping. No one in my stable hates on the next hoe spot because she knows that hoe been with me, and for me as well. By the time I finished running down the game to Sara, we were pulling up at McDonalds when I seen a bunch of amigos hanging in the parking lot as if they was looking for Michelle.

I passed the garbage can she was hiding in when I got a call for her whispering, "Daddy, I just seen you went pass. The Mexican wallet I took is standing with the shirt off and short pants on. They think I'm in the girls restroom inside McDonalds.

"Okay, stay in there bitch until I tell you to come out." I sent Sara to the Mexican Michelle stole from and told her to seduce him into wanting to take her with him. The plan worked. Soon as he seen Sara, his mind completely forgot about Michelle. They both walked off into the apartment holding one another. You would have thought this bitch Michelle was Oscar The Grouch from The Sesame Street the way she came out the garbage can smiling with a bankroll. She hopped in the back seat and said, "OH SHIT DADDY, I smell like trash!" I looked over my shoulder and said, "no you don't! You smell like Cash!" We both laughed as we disappear behind the tint.

Daddy, who was that white girl that got out your car?"

"That's Sara baby, your new in-law I said. "She's Pretty," Michelle said. "I like the way she moved that Mexican. That was right on time!" Before we could get on the expressway, Sara was calling saying, "I got a hundred dollars from that Mexican.

He claimed that's all he had, because some hoe just robbed him for four thousand dollars. Daddy, is it true? Did Michelle get him for that much money?" I smiled through the phone and said, "Nah Baby girl, she didn't get him for everything, because he still had a hundred dollars to give to you."

"WOW!" She said, "I can't wait until I take that much money!"

"Meet me at the same McDonald's you got out the car at," I said.

When we pulled up on the scene, Melissa remembered to sit in the right spot she was in my life. Soon as Sara got in the car she said to Michelle, "I haven't met you yet, but you are a cold ass bitch! How did you do it?" Michelle blushed, she never had any of her in-laws make her feel like she was special. She said to Sara, "Don't give me the credit sweetie, I owe it all to my Daddy! He taught me Everything! I'm sure within time he will show you some finesse moves." They both sat in the back laughing on how the trick was looking when he realized his money was gone. Twenty minutes after one o'clock was the time when the girls and I made it back up to the apartment. The rest of the girls was still up watching this movie called *"Scarface."* **Soon as Infinity seen me she asked, "Daddy, may I talk with you?"**

"Not now Infinity. I'm going in my room to think for a minute."

"Well, I just wanted to apologize to you and Sara for acting the way I did today."

"Bitch, you know how I feel about that sorry shit. DON'T TELL ME, SHOW ME! Now you can go rundown that sorry shit to that bitch and see will she go for that shit."

Infinity knew that I was tired of her possessive ways, and if she couldn't control her feelings, there was no way was she going to last.

For the last few hours, I had done so much Pimping until I forgot that I was supposed to been picking up Goldy Locs. I attempted to call him but there was no answer on his end. I knew that I had a busy day coming up in the morning, so I jumped in my master king bed to catch up on some more Pimp Rest.

Chapter 21

Top of the morning Jazz woke me up saying, "Daddy, someone knocked at the door, then left and went downstairs now is blowing their horn outside. I immediately leaped to my feet and looked out my window. It was Goldy's hoe Dana walking around a brand-new Cadillac Sedan Deville! The person who was blowing the horn was a Pimp! Ah Shit! Not just a Pimp, it's my partner Goldy Locs jumping out, popping, screaming Pimping loud as he could. When I went downstairs, Dana was still walking around the car as if she was crazy. But the bitch wasn't crazy, she was showing off the brand-new Cadillac that she just gave birth to. Goldy greeted me with his arms out in a position as if he wanted to dance. I locked arms with him as we danced off Curtis Mayfield singing, *"The Life We Live Is Beautiful."* All of my hoes was looking down from their windows smiling and showing cheers.

From the outside looking in you would say my hoes was out of pocket for being excited about the next Pimp fame, but when you really on the inside of the game it's a spirit that support one another. They knew if I was out there dancing, then Daddy is happy about something, they going to dance too! This made Dana feel like anything was possible! She came from a country little spot in Crestview, FL. Making $4.35 an hour, and now working the track where hoes get famous at, giving birth to houses and automobiles, no babies! Even if she would ever leave Goldy, she will never leave the game after being exposed to the finest things in life. "Breakfast on me!" Goldy said as he told Dana she can get back in the car. "Mac Goldie Mane, I owe you my life! Because that's what you put back in me (LIFE)…" "Mane stop giving me the credit when it was you that put your game down on that bitch and came up!"

Goldy looked at me and said, "Yeah you Right, it was my Pimping huh?" We both laughed then I said, "Give me a minute Goldy to get myself together. Would you like to come up stairs?"

"Nah I'm cool Goldie. I'm going to wait for you out here, while I listen to Curtis telling it like it is."

Goldy was happy to be back alive, and you can see it! Pretty as the color and nice as the car looked, it was something about it that made it look beautiful, which was a Pimp and his hoe." When I went back upstairs Jazz was standing in the kitchen with a question.

"Daddy, isn't that the new turn out bitch that was working over there with me?"

"Sure, is hoe, she just gave birth to that new Cadillac out there."

"That's what's up," Jazz said.

You see in this Game, there's no room for hate. If you Pimping like you suppose to on your hoe and she hoeing like she supposed to for your Pimping, it's going to show up in the lights.

Goldy Locs good news made me feel like I just charge the bitch for something

Great! I put on my Butterfly Coogi Short Set With my Bumblebee Alligator Sandals. Yes! I was going to Pimp with my friend in his brand new 1998 Cadillac Sedan Deville!

To see another player, rise from the bottom back on his way to the top always done something to me. What I mean is, my best relationship with a Pimp is when he didn't have nothing but what was in him. No flow, no hoe, no wheels, NOTHING! Nothing but his game and his belief. You see a square will go for anything. You can have over five girls with the tools we use to bring a bitch in, and to an outsider they will say, damn, that's a real player right there! WHY? Because they are squares that don't know the inside of the game. I said what I said to say this, you never going to know if your Pimp friend is a Pimp unless you catch him at the bottom Pimping his way back up! Or if he done already made his way to the top, and has all the tools to trick a fool, then the only way you going to know if he's a Pimp or not is to knock a bitch he cares about. Then, sit back to see if the sucker comes out of him or the Pimping! Don't be surprise, if the friend you been knowing for over 10 years act like a sucker about that Bitch!

Goldy and I have only known each other less than a month, but each day we kicked it, it felt like I been Pimping with him for years. We rode the new caddy through downtown underground, back down the track where hoes were already working, and back out to Mexican Land where Dana got out to work.

Once she exited the car, I turned down the music and said to Goldy, "Pimping, I just want to congratulate you on your Pimping. The time we put into one another definitely paid off. The only way to go now is to the top. Safety first through Pimping! Protect yourself!" "I can dig it Mac Goldie. So, tell me Goldie, how is everything going with that bitch you came up with from Greyhound?"

"Who you talking about my little bitty bitch name Sara? Aw mane I think she's going to be an alright hooker. She feels like this is her home and this is where she wants to be. She has good mannerisms and conduct. Also, her first day she came in with $1100. But you know just like I do Goldy Locs, these hoes have a heads and tails about themselves. Right now, the hoe just showing me heads on the coin. I haven't seen her how she acts when the coin lands on tails. Goldy Locs laugh and said, "You sure right about that!"

After Goldy and I finish from having breakfast and riding through the city I told him to drop me off at my spot. He still was trying to pay me back the money I had given him, but I refuse to take it. I didn't give him the money for him to pay me back, I gave it to him so he wouldn't lose his place and for him to get back on his feet.

"Call me later Mac Goldie, I'm going back downtown to see can I catch up with Slick Frank."

I said, "I sure will Pimping, "don't you and Frank do too much Pimping without me." I watch him pulled off in his pretty automobile that he Pimped for.

When I walked in the apartment, Sara was up by herself watching this show call *"Let's Make A Deal."*

"Hi Daddy," she said reaching her arms out for me to hug her.

"What's up baby girl? What you doing up all by yourself?" She showed me her phone with all the missed calls that her ex-boyfriend had call.

"Daddy, he's been calling me all morning, I wouldn't answer. I really would like to get my number changed if it's ok with you?"

"For your honesty and loyalty Sara, we sure will change your number. We don't need no distractions. Since you up Sara, come sit down with me, so I can run some things down to you on the area you will be working." She cut me off saying, "but Daddy, I like the area you had me and Infinity working yesterday."

"Chill Baby," I said. "Anywhere that I put you down, you should be able to come up! It's my job to lace you up with plays to help you score and win on the field." She cut me off again this time saying, "I love the way you break down the game to me as if it's a real game! For instance, when you say, you're going to give me the play to help score and win. That sounds like we playing a real game!" All I could do was look Sara in her big blue square eyes and say, "Baby, this is a real game. And for the last time, it's time you take it serious."

"I'm sorry, I didn't mean to upset you," Sara said. I just love the way you lacing me up Daddy." I gently grabbed her by the head and rubbed my fingers through her silky hair and said, "Baby, you still a square and unaware of how serious this game can get. That's what I'm here for, to make sure you don't hit the field not knowing the play. We don't want you playing basketball on a football field Right?" She smiled and said "Right."

Then said, "Daddy, you just have a way of putting words and I love It!"

I mentioned before what makes a good teacher, is a good student. Sara was definitely turning me on with her enthusiasm for the game. I noticed my pager was constantly beeping with a code on it, it read 187. This code meant "Murder" and I definitely wanted to know who in the fuck would page me this! I called the number back and it was my half pimping cousin Fly Ty.

"What's up Kinfolks?" he said as I can hear him laughing through the phone. "You thought I was somebody who wanted to blow your ass off when I left the code 187 huh?"

"FLY MOTHERFUCKING TY!" I said through the phone! Mane, I didn't know who the fuck you was playing like that! I thought you was this new bitch boyfriend done got my number and now ready to kill a PIMP!" Fly Ty laughed harder this time then said, "Kinfolks, come pick me up. I'm at Greyhound. I'll tell you the rest when I see you." Although, I knew my cousin Ty wasn't no full-blooded Pimp, I still loved for him to ride with me and have my back. He was a good spirit to feel close to me. I took Sara with me since she was already up, plus I wanted to finish lacing her up with the game.

She cut in asking, "Daddy, can I come up front with you so that I can be right beside you?"

I asked her jokingly, "Are you still a stranger in my life baby? Because remember, the front seat is a stranger seat."

"Well, where is your cousin going to sit? Is he a stranger?" she asked? She was being sarcastic and nosey which was getting out of pocket. So, I put her quickly back in pocket when I said, "Listen to me good Sara! My friends are not your friends UNDERSTAND! You don't worry about nobody but me and you understand!" She quickly said "YES" and sat back silently in the seat.

Chapter 22

When we pulled up at Greyhound, I saw Fly from a mile away. He stood six foot six taller than everyone in the station. He noticed my car then threw his arms up waving. Soon as he got in the car, he noticed Sara and spoke, "HI PRETTY," he said.

"Hello," Sara said back.

"BITCH! Didn't I just tell you my friends are not yours?" She grabbed both of her hands putting them on her face then said, "I'M SORRY, I FORGOT!" This was all Ty needed to see, was a fresh loose bitch of mines speaking to him. He continued talking saying, "Cuz Mane, you not going to believe what happened to me in Memphis!"

"What Mane?" I asked out of concern.

"My Stupid ass baby mommy tricked me to come stay a night with her, and when I fell asleep, she called the police on me. Then woke me up talking about, police at the door for you putting your hands on me last week. Mane I had to jump out the window, plus run from the dogs." Once again, Sara got out of pocket and burst out laughing off what Ty just said. I asked Ty to chill for a minute, then said to Sara, "Say bitch, you doing a lot of out-of-pocket shit back there. Are you sure this is where you want to be?"

"Yes Daddy," she said still smiling at Ty.

Sara was too fresh for me to slap the eyeballs out of her motherfucking head. As bad as I wanted to, I couldn't do it. Instead, I played cool and told Ty he can finish with his conversation. He looked at the bitch to see was she still looking, then he went on continue telling more stories hoping to get her out of pocket again.

Anyone that knows the game would have said, "I was wrong for bringing a fresh bitch around a fun ass nigga, but that's something you're not going to be able to control, and that's an out-of-pocket hoe! Especially, that's into niggas! I wasn't taking Ty back to the apartment because there wasn't enough room for him there, so I offered to get him a room. "Dig this Ty, I'm going to get you a room over there in Mexican Land. I might need you to let the girls use your room if they don't have nowhere to date them."

"Cool Kinfolks, I'll just step out whenever you call and tell me one of them has a date."

"Okay Cool," I said.

Once I finished from getting Ty situated, Sara and I headed back to the apartment. The whole way there I said nothing to her, and she did the same to me. She knew that I was upset with her, but the squareness that was still in the bitch didn't care. Bitch didn't have no respect for me or The Game!

All of the girls was up when Sara and I came in as they all spoke to the both of us, "Good evening Daddy, Hello Sara." Sara didn't speak back as if she had an attitude with me, so I said, "Say bitch, you don't hear your sisters speaking to you?"

"OH, I'm sorry guys! My mind must have been somewhere else, hello everybody!" she said. All of the girls were hip to when one of them has been with me alone then come back sad meant, *I must have got into her shit about something.*

Infinity loved to see me Pimp hard on a white bitch because it made her feel like I wasn't just hard on her because she was black. In the corner I seen her with a smirk look on her face. It was two o'clock in the afternoon and I was trying to debate on whether or not should I leave town with Jazz and the girls but leave Sara and Melissa here to play Mexican Land.

Sara was still into her feelings with a blanket over her head as if she were trying to segregate herself from the family. When I snatched the blanket off her head, she jumped as if she was hiding something. I noticed someone was on the phone she was talking to, look at this shit. This bitch on the phone with her ex-boyfriend *(GINUWINE).*

"GIVE ME MY PHONE BACK!" Sara yelled!! "BITCH YOU BETTER WATCH YOUR MOTHERFUCKING MOUTH!" Infinity said to Sara. I might couldn't have slap the shit out of Sara because she was too fresh for me to trust, but this didn't stop Infinity from wanting to beat her ass.

"HELLO!" I said to her boyfriend on the phone.

"WHO IS THIS?" he said back trying to sound like a killer!

"This is a Pimp, cock sucker, you need to come get your girlfriend! Both of y'all need to get your square asses back in the box and play with one another." The sucker was so lame he didn't comprehend what I was saying and said, "WHAT YOU SAY NIGGA? I didn't understand you!"

"I know you didn't COCK SUCKER, so what do that tells you? TO STAY IN YOUR MOTHERFUCKIN' LANE!" Then I threw the phone at Sara and told her to get her shit AND GET THE FUCK OUT MY

HOUSE! She begged me to not kick her out, but no way I was going to let a faggot disrespect "My Pimping!" I told all the girls, "Get that Bitch Shit, and take her back to greyhound."

"Daddy, please no! Please, I'm Sorry. I will never disrespect your Pimping again! Please!" The bitch said please so many times, she was starting to sound like James Brown.

"Bitch stop all that begging and take your ass in the bathroom and get yourself together. And when you come out! I don't want to see a tear in your eyes, YOU UNDERSTAND ME?"

"Yes Daddy, I Do. Thank You for forgiving me!"

"GET OUT MY FACE! SQUARE ASS BITCH!"

Sara hadn't been with me a whole 72 hours and done already made me get in her shit! *I wonder if this bitch is going to be a problem.* First, she got out of pocket with Fly Ty, then come home and do this shit! Melissa liked her and was the first one to

205

embrace her with welcome arms again. She followed her into the restroom whispering to her saying, "Girl, don't ever do no shit like that again!" The rest of the girls watched her with furious eyes as if they wanted to attack her. I had lost all interest in Sara and didn't give a damn if she went to work and never came back. But my dedication for the game wouldn't allow me to neglect a hoe who needed my Pimping.

I decided that I was going to let Melissa and Sara stay here in Atlanta and work Mexican Land for the weekend, while Jazz, Michelle, and Infinity come with me to North Carolina. It was still too early in the game to leave a fresh bitch like Sara by herself. But I Pimped real fast and expected my hoes to catch on quick! I will give a bitch like Sara this type of distance just to see was she going to get out of pocket again or just go another way with her bullshit.

Right when I was debating on what I wanted to do about Sara, Fly Ty called saying, "Kinfolks, you better hurry and bring them hoes over here Mane! It's a gang of these construction working Mexicans just checked into the hotel. They just asked me do I have any girls working? What you want me to tell them Kinfolks?"

"Tell them to chill for about 30 minutes to an hour, some pretty girls will be over there soon."

"Dig That Kinfolks," Ty said.

After hanging up with Fly, I called Melissa and Sara in the living room to give them a rundown on where they're going to be working. "Dig this Girls, I'm leaving for the weekend to take the rest of the girls to North Carolina. Melissa, you and Sara are going to stay here and work over in Mexican Land. My Cousin Fly Ty has a room you two can use just in case you have nowhere to take your date."

I looked into Sara eyes and read her thoughts; she was hoping to come with me out of town but knew she couldn't. She wasn't sure if I still wanted her after the out of pocket shit she did earlier. Melissa she's cool, she showed no emotion about me having her to stay here with Sara.

Sara barely whispered, "Daddy, may I speak with you before you leave?"

"Go head hoe, I'm listening."

She took a deep breath than said, "Daddy, I'm really sorry about earlier. I promise that will never happen again!"

I didn't blink not once when I looked her in the eyes and said, "I hear you talking hoe, but you going to have to show me through your conduct and trap, you understand?"

"Yes Daddy," she said. This time smiling, feeling like I had forgiven her.

Melissa also wanted to rap with me before I left, "Daddy, are you leaving at this moment?"

"No, why what's up baby?"

"Daddy, I don't mean to sound like an ungrateful bitch, but it's been a while since I had the chance to be one on one with you. Please don't get mad for me asking, but when you come back can we do something together Daddy?" Usually, I would have cursed Melissa the fuck out for asking me for some square time with her. But I knew she has been patient for at least four months to be around me, so I said, "sure, my baby angel. Not only am I going to spend some time with you, I'm also going to make you feel real good for having patience and understanding." She smiled and kissed my fist saying, "Daddy, you're the best!"

I instructed the girls to get their things together so that I could drop them off at Fly Ty room. The rest of the girls was excited about going out of town with me to work. Suddenly, Jazz received a phone call from a trick that comes in town every month and gives her and two more girls $500 apiece. She got off the phone as if she heard some bad news. When in actuality, the news was good! It just killed her spirit when this put a delay on our trip out of town. I wasn't going to tell Sara or Melissa that my plans had changed. I wanted to see was Sara going to be loyal to me while I was gone. They waited on me patiently in the car while I finish rapping with the girls.

"Michelle, you and Infinity are going to work again together. This time in Cobb County. I don't want Sara to know that we stayed here, so if she happens to call either of you, don't answer!" Infinity was looking like she was depress about something, so I said, "You okay Hoe?"

"Yes, Daddy I'm cool. I was really ready to leave Atlanta for a minute and go somewhere else like, California!"

"Damn bitch," I said. "You think you ready for that west coast hoeing?"

"Yes Daddy," she said. "I'm ready to show you with your game I could go anywhere in this world and hoe up!"

Infinity was a true definition of a Memphis Bitch. Down for her man, will break her back to get her man some money, and had a heart that was braver than a man.

When I went to the car Melissa and Sara was laughing and building a wifey relationship. Soon as I got in the car Melissa hit me with a question, "Daddy, do you want Sara and I to work together or separate?"

"Separate," I said. "But if she should need you than exchange numbers so that she can reach you."

"Yes Daddy," she said sounding excited still from the news I told her earlier.

When we pulled into the hotel there was a gang of Mexicans everywhere in the parking lot. When they seen the girls they all start gathering in one straight line asking how much? Sara couldn't believe all these Mexicans wanted to date her. I believe her pussy spoke out before her thoughts did and asked, "DO I HAVE TO FUCK ALL OF THEM?"

"Nah Bitch," I said.

"You don't fuck them like you trying to bust a nut, you flip them within 7 to 10 minutes. Flip means, put him on his back or he put you on yours, but flip his ass real quick like a pancake and get his ass out the way."

Sara smiled and said, "I told you Daddy that I love the way you break down the game."

"Me Too," Melissa said, "Isn't he a genius?" Soon as I let the girls out, they both was grabbed by a group of Mexicans ready to fuck.

Fly Ty eyes was popping out of his head in disbelief of what he was seeing. "Goddamn kinfolks, I need me a hoe mane! All these motherfucking Mexicans with this money! Kinfolks, please let me rob one these motherfuckers!"

"Slow down Fly Ty," I said. "We already robbing their ass with this white pussy I have for sell." I continued to say, "You right about one thing though, you do need a hoe instead of a gun."

Like I said earlier, Fly Ty wasn't a true bonified Pimp, so anything goes for him in the game. "Dig this Fly Ty, how bout we take a ride downtown and let these hoes take care of my business.

"Okay Cool," Ty said, "Let me get my phone out the room."

On the way downtown, I was running down to Fly Ty that if he stayed down and stay true to the game that the game will be true to him. Nodding his head and rolling a blunt at the same time he said "You right kinfolks! Mane all I need is a HOE! Starting today I'm going to holler at every bitch I come across."

I knew Fly wasn't sincere about what he was saying, but it sounded real good. Something like a good dream," he was real funny and good company to have around. But when he came across a hoe, he would give her his heart before his Pimping. He never claimed to be a full-blooded Pimp, only a Mack mixed with a player. Anytime he felt that he couldn't handle a bitch that came across his path he would pass the ball to me. He definitely was a player.

Chapter 23

Fly Ty and I left downtown on our way to pick up the girls from the house. As we were riding Fly said, "Kinfolks, how you manage to handle five girls at the same time? I mean, don't them hoes be jealous of one another sometimes."

"Dig this Fly Ty, when you dealing with these hoes you can't be playing no games with their hearts. You know a woman is already emotional, so why would you fill her mind and heart up with a bunch of square bullshit that will affect her hoeing? You see Fly, all a real hoe wants from a Pimp is some understanding and for him to stand on what he believes in. Also, keep your swipe out of her!"

He interrupted me and said, "MY SWIPE! What's that?"

"Your swipe is the little head that takes control of the big head when she wants to fuck! It's not healthy at all Fly Ty to bring a hoe in off your dick! It will only make her slow and worry about what you doing instead of handling your business."

He put both hands on top of his head and said, "Oh now I see, you can't fuck your girls at all right?"

"No, wrong again!" I said to Fly. "Tell me Ty, if you don't have sex with your girls then who you going to give yourself to, a square?"

He looked confused then said, "Damn Kinfolks, I never thought about it that way."

I told him, "I know you didn't green ass nigga, because you just a squirrel trying to bust a nut." We both laughed as the girls was headed to the car.

"Hi Ty," Jazz said when she got in the car. Jazz was the only one allowed to speak to Ty, the rest of the girls couldn't.

The reason Jazz was allowed to speak with him was because she been around long enough to know him like I do. But just because she could talk to him, she still didn't take advantage of it. She respected him as a man and carried herself like a lady around him. Fly Ty also respected Jazz and wouldn't disrespect her. He had the upmost respect for her after watching Jazz grow with me over the years. He knew that Jazz was my M.V.P. Player in this game. "What's up Jazz," Ty said speaking back. After they spoke to one another they both got back serious and didn't say nothing else. They didn't want the girls feeling like it was okay to speak and kick it with Fly Ty. Although he wasn't a Pimp, this still wasn't healthy to have a friendly friendship.

Jazz broke the silence when she said, "Daddy, remember that trick that called me earlier, he wants to see me and Michelle. I asked about Infinity, but he claims his partner backed out at the last minute." Jazz and Infinity wasn't good with working together, so of course, Jazz came up with a terrific lie to keep Infinity from going. Infinity peeped game and said, "Like you said Daddy, it's the trick lost not mines."

Ty was sitting on the side of me as if he wanted to laugh, but he remained froze. What Infinity had said made him want to say something. He couldn't believe the little time that Infinity had been with me, how much she had grown. After dropping Jazz and Michelle off, Ty and I took Infinity to Midtown to work. Ponce De Leon was the track in Midtown for a hoe to get some money. Soon as she hit the track, there were an older white guy sitting in Krispy Kreme parking lot waiting for her. After she was out the car, Ty said what he wanted to say.

"Damn kinfolks, you got that Infinity bitch game tight! That bitch starting to sound just like you."

I agreed with Ty and said, "Yea Fly Ty, that bitch growing, but she still has some growing to do."

"Dig that, kinfolks dig that." Fly Ty said as he reached his hand out to shake mines. In the middle of us conversing, I received a phone call from my hoe Melissa.

"Hi Daddy,"

"What's happening baby?" I said.

"Daddy I haven't seen Sara, hopefully that's a good thing right," She asked?

"Yea," I said. "What's going on with you though?" I asked?

"Everything is good Daddy, I have five hundred right now, and this Mexican wants to take me to his room for five. That will be my thousand dollars, Daddy. Can I go?"

"Sure, Baby Star, take care of your business baby. Once you finish, catch a cab back to the house."

"Yes sir," she said sounding excited! After I hung up from Melissa, Sara was calling on the other end.

"Hello," I said.

"Hey Daddy," Sara said sounding depressed. "Daddy, I only have three hundred and twenty-five dollars, these Mexican are cheap, and plus they stink!"

"Bitch, you sound like you making love to them Mexicans! Where are you now?" I asked?

"I'm still in the same apartments, and Daddy I'm not making love to these nasty ass Mexicans. They just stink and always trying to kiss on me. I'm trying Daddy. I'm going to get your thousand, okay?"

"Ok," I said. "Once you get your thousand, go back to Ty room and I'll be through there to get you."

"Yes Daddy, thank you," she said.

"Dig this Fly Ty, I need to drop you off at your room for a minute while I go handle some business."

"Ok, cool kinfolks," Ty said. "Is everything alright? You sure you don't need me to ride with you," he asked?

"Nah, I'm cool kinfolks. I just need to make a stop and rap with a friend of mines."

"Dig that Cuz," Ty said. "Well, if you need me, you know where I'm at."

Chapter 24

I hadn't heard from Goldy Locs in some days. I know how unpredictable this game can be. You can be here today and gone tomorrow. So, I decided to give him a call to see if he was he okay. I called twice and let the phone ring over ten times, still no answer. Since I was in the area where he stayed, I pulled over to check on him. When I pulled into the hotel Goldy was sitting inside his car with his head down as if he had nodded off. I tapped my horn on the car like a Pimp then I screamed out the window, "GET UP PIMPING, AIN'T NO SLEEPING ON THE JOB!" Goldy Locs raised up and gave me half of a smile. Then said, "Mac Goldie, My Friend. What's happening baby?"
"Mane I've been calling you. You okay?" I noticed on his radio he was listening to *The Temptations.* **This song called,** *have you seen her?* **"You okay baby,"** I asked again? **"Yeah, Mac Goldie I'm cool mane! That**

punk fat bitch of mines been gone for two days and no one has called me about the bitch telling me she's okay. I believe the big bitch still around here hoeing, because when I went over to Mexican Land one of the Amigo's asked me was she still busy in one of the apartments." He paused for a moment and then turned his music up a little louder as the Temptation's continued asking in the song, *Have you seen her?* "Mac Goldie Mane, can you believe that big bitch was conning me the whole time like I was the best thing that happened to her? I even put her on a diet, one hotdog a day." I cut him off shouting "WHAT DID YOU SAY? You only feed the big bitch a hotdog a day? MANE! That big bitch hasn't went nowhere but to McDonald's somewhere for two days. Ain't no Pimp going to call you about that hoe. Ronald McDonald got your bitch!" We both laughed as he got out the car back on his feet Pimping again. He gave me a *Spirit Hug* then said, "Mac Goldie Mane, you sure know how to get a brother back to Pimping!" I looked at him and said,

"As long as I'm alive, I'm going to make sure you stay on top of your game baby. How about we bend some corners and see can we spot that big bitch of yours in one of these McDonald's lines?" We laughed again then drove off into the Atlanta traffic.

I was running down to Goldy about the issues that I had with Sara. "Mane, that little frisky friendly new bitch I have is still a green bean in the game. I know it's my job to tighten the lame bitch up, but in between all that slow shit, she wants to be loose with it."

"What did the bitch do?" Goldy asked?

"Nothing that a Pimp can't straighten out," I answered. "She just wants a little physical attention. I have her now over in Mexican Land by herself. Hopefully, them Mexicans wear her out until all she wants to do is come in and go straight to sleep."

It was close to three o'clock in the morning, after Goldy and I went separate ways. I'm glad that I was able to see him before leaving town because there was no telling when I was coming back. After dropping him off, I headed toward Fly Ty room to check on Sara. When I opened the door, they both was sleeping in the same bed. I skipped past Ty and tapped Sara on her shoulders saying, "say bitch, what the fuck going on?"

"OH, SHIT DADDY! I didn't know he was over here." She acted as if she didn't. Fly Ty woke up saying the same thing, that he didn't know how she got in his bed. So, I took Sara into the restroom to talk with her, "Listen bitch, I don't play these funny Bugs Bunny games! Now if you like this man, then bitch choose up! Don't think that you or him can be around here slick liking one another. The name of the game is CHOOSE BITCH!"

After I finished talking to Sara, I told Ty to take a ride with me real quick.

"Let me grab my phone," Ty said looking leery. Once he stepped outside, I already knew what I wanted to say to him, which was, *"get the fuck out my life!"* but I didn't. That would have been a sucker response. So instead, I stayed cool and said, "Dig

This Fly, you know I don't play no games with these hoes, and I don't let them play no games with me." Before he could say anything, I said, "Hold on and let me finish what I have to say. I need you to rundown the truth to me on what happen with you two while I was gone?"

"Nothing kinfolks, I swear. All I know is when I got up to use the restroom, she was in the bed with me." He continued to say, "I thought you told the bitch to get over there, because I know how you don't let a fresh bitch sleep with you. Foreal kinfolks! I'm telling you the truth." Between them two big hokey eyes of his, I seen that he wasn't lying. I knew that Sara had a liking for Ty the first time she saw him. So, I fault myself for putting her around him being the immature hoe she was at the time.

Ty and I left to go to my house. While leaving, Sara sat there in the room by herself. I could feel Fly Ty vibe wanting to stay at the room with Sara. He was a reptile, but he wasn't a snake. You know the kind that would bite you after you done helped him. So, he played cool and went along with me to the apartment. All of the girls had already made it to the apartment sitting in the living room watching the movie Scarface.

"Hi Daddy, where is Sara?" Melissa asked.

"Bitch, worry about your own ass!" I said.

"Sorry Daddy, I was just asking."

Each one of the girls came one by one handing me their trap. Five thousand and eighty-five dollars is what the girls gave me that night. Ty big hokey eyes seen everything.

"Damn kinfolks, let me hold something?" I peeled off a couple of hundreds and passed it to him. Like I said earlier, Fly Ty wasn't a Pimp, but he was great company to have around.

That following day, Ty and I headed back over to his room to check on Sara. She looked as if she stayed up all night worried about what's going to happen.

"Good Morning Daddy," she spoke, but only to see was I still mad with her. I said nothing to her as if she didn't exist. For attention, she wanted me to break her jaw, but I was ready to break her feelings. When you in this life, it's two ways you can take this game, personal or business. If you take it too personal than you will react with emotion, but if you play it like a business, then your reaction would be done off devotion.

"Get yourself together Sara, you going to work early today," I said.

"Where am I working Daddy?" she asked being curious.

"Same spot you played yesterday, Bitch! Now get yourself together like I said and don't ask me shit else!" She knew from my spirit that I was still upset with her, so she said, "Sorry, I didn't mean to make you upset." When I left her last night, I forgot to get the money she made yesterday, but she reminded me with a twelve-hundred-dollar trap she placed in my hand.

"Here Daddy, you forgot to get your money last night." I didn't count it as if it meant nothing to me. I was raising Sara to know how to respect me before she paid me.

"Daddy, may I have a few dollars to buy more condoms and something to eat?" she asked. I peeled off fifty dollars from the trap she gave me and said, "Once you finish eating go back to where you was yesterday, I'm sure them same Mexicans would love to see you again." From the look on her face, I could read what was on her mind, she thought to herself, *damn I got to deal with these Mexicans again?* But still she showed no emotion toward my instructions.

"Daddy, may I speak with you before you leave?"

"Sure, what's up?" She looked at me as if she wanted to talk in private, so I said to Fly Ty, "Dig this Kinfolks, give me a minute to rap with my people."

Soon as Ty left out the room, she rushed me with opened arms saying, "Daddy, please forgive me about last night." Without hugging her back I said in a cold spirt, "I'm going to forgive you bitch this time, but go get my money first!"

"Yes Daddy," She said as if I had already forgave her.

Fly Ty was already sitting in the car when I came outside. I noticed on the radio he was listening to this song by Too Short, *I Never Let A Hoe Pimp Me."* He was bobbing his head and popping his collar as if he had some Pimp Bones. Being around me had Fly Ty wanting to Pimp! What he didn't know was, I made the game look easy because everything was done proper and organized. But the game was far from being easy! It's like you really have to have the heart and stomach to Pimp!! What Fly Ty didn't know was, this Game will show you a beautiful picture just to bring you in. It also will sometimes give you five years of fame, then come back and take 20 years of your life. Just remember this, if you really on the inside of the Game and really doing some Pimping, the Game will give you any and everything you desire. In return, the Game wants either one of the three things back from you —Your freedom, Your life, or to make you lose your motherfucking mind!! Once you done Pimped long enough to have knowledge and understanding about The Game then you have a choice.

Fly Ty turned down the volume on the radio and said "Kinfolks, I got to get me a hoe Mane!"

I looked over to him and gave him some words of advice saying, "Dig this Fly Ty, as long as you stay true to this this game and believe in yourself, so that someone will believe in you. I guarantee, The Game is going to bless you."

Before I could finish telling him some more about the game, I was interrupted by a phone call from Sara.

"Hello," I said.

"Hello, Hi Daddy this Sara."

"Bitch I know who this is! What's up with you?" She asked was Fly Ty still around me.

"Yeah, bitch why?"

"Daddy, remember what you said the other night? About if I liked Fly Ty that I need to get him some money?" Not really understanding what this hoe is trying to say I said, "Hold on bitch, let me turn this music down. Now what the fuck you just said?" She didn't hesitate to say it again, this time she put some emphasis on it saying, "I said that I want to give Ty this money!" Fly Ty was un-aware of what was going on and I was stunned to the news this bitch was trying to serve me. "Where you at now hoe?" I asked. "Behind McDonald's in these apartments. Are you coming to get me or Ty?" she asked?

"BITCH JUST COME TO MCDONALDS!" I said. *How should I handle this situation?* I knew Ty wasn't a full bloody Pimp and that he knew nothing about what Sara wanted to give him. "Dig this Ty, remember me telling you if you stayed down you will soon come up?" He shook head while rolling a blunt and said, "Dig that kinfolk!" As we were talking, I seen Sara coming out the apartment behind McDonalds smiling. She hopped in the back seat excited like the first day she chose me, "Do I give it to him myself?" Sara asked.

"Give it to who you want to be with Bitch!" She reached over Fly Ty shoulders and handed him an eight hundred dollars trap.

"Here you are Fly-Ty. I want to be with you! Not believing what had just happened, Ty looked at me and said, "What's Going on Kinfolks?"

"What do you mean what's going on nigga? Looks like the bitch trying to pay you."

Immediately Ty gave her instructions to get out the car. It hasn't been twenty minutes went pass and Fly Ty already think he's a Pimp.

Once Sara was out the car, Fly Ty looked over at me and said again, "for real kinfolks, what's going on?" I explained to him what I told Sara the other night, "I said Bitch! If you want to be with my cousin then get him some money, and do it the right way, CHOOSE UP! So, I guess she went out the door for you today."

Still shocked, Fly Ty shook his head and said, "Damn kinfolks, you real mane. I'm going to step out and talk with this bitch Kinfolks about this move she just made. Give me a couple of hours, I'm going to give you call."

I watched Fly Ty disappear with my hoe and thought to myself, *Did I do the right thing by letting her go? Of course, I did!* Although Ty wasn't a Pimp, I still couldn't stop her from wanting to give him some money. The whole scene was too fast for me to embrace. I stayed parked in the same spot for a long thirty minutes, still not believing what just happened. I had to get out of my emotions and get back focused. This wasn't the first time or last time that a bitch choose up with someone. I wasn't going to let one hoe stop my show.

Chapter 25

When I came back to the house without Sara, Melissa looked *"curious,"* but as she would say, *"SHE'S CONCERNED."* Before she could say anything, I answered her curiosity and said, "Bitch! You don't have to worry about working with that Sara bitch, she's not with us anymore." "Foreal Daddy? THAT UNGRATEFUL BITCH!"

When it came to hoes leaving a Pimp, after she has built a real sisterhood with their in-laws, hoes take it more personal than a Pimp would. To a Pimp, it was all business, but to a hoe, it was personal!

That following next day Fly Ty was up before a rooster could crow, calling me saying, "Kinfolks, get up mane, the early bird gets the worm."

"What's happening Fly Ty?" I said. "Looks like you in good spirit this morning!" Still screaming through the phone Fly Ty said, "Mane this Sara bitch really getting A Pimp some money!" He continued to say,

"She's acting like this is where she wanted to be." I knew Fly Ty was trying to make me feel some type of way from what he was telling me, but I felt no emotions toward his rundown about Sara. It's true, I hated that I wasn't the one she was giving her money to, but never once did I hate him for breaking the bitch. You see, in order to become a "Great Pimp," you must know how to respect the next Player when it's his turn to charge the bitch.

"DIG THAT!" I said to Fly Ty. "Well Fly Ty I'm going to give you some time with your hoe, so that you can get what you need out of her. I know as long as you around me, I'm going to be a distraction to the hoe. So, the girls and I might ride up to North Carolina for a few days."

"Dig that kinfolks." TY SAID.

"Kinfolks, do you mind if we stayed in your apartment until you get back?"

First, I wanted to tell Fly Ty HELL NAH! Then I thought about this being his first hoe, that he could use all the help he can get.

"Sure Fly," I said. "I'll leave the key to the apartment, and whatever you do, DON'T GO IN MY ROOM!"

"10-4 KINFOLKS! I promise to stay away from the room."

When I got off the phone with Fly Ty. I noticed Infinity standing in my doorway. I wondered to myself, *how loBitng have this bitch been standing there? And I wonder if she heard what I was talking to Fly about?* I tested her and said, "Damn bitch, how long you been there?"

"I just got up Daddy," She lied. "Can I ask you something Daddy?"

"Sure, what's on your mind?" She took a deep breath then said, "Is Sara still down with us?" "Bitch, I thought you said you wasn't listening to my conversation?"

"I wasn't Daddy! I promise! Melissa told me last night. I just hate when bitches do shit like this Daddy!"

"It's part of the game baby," I reminded Infinity. "Now go back outside and tell the girls we leaving today, going up North." Infinity leaped to her feet and jumped up like a cheerleader when I said we was going out of town. You would have thought that she was on her way to Disney World, the way she skipped through the house screaming to the girls, "PACK YOUR THINGS SISTERS, WE'RE GOING OUT OF TOWN!"

"Where we going Daddy?" Michelle asked. "With me bitch," I replied in a good spirit. Jazz still had her door shut when all of the excitement was going on.

"Damn could you guys chill with all the noise!" Jazz opened her door yelling out. "Who you talking to bitch? Its only one king in this house, Now get your ass up and pack your shit."

"Daddy, what did I do? Don't put me out! I'm just tired and have a bad headache."

"BITCH! Who said something about putting you out? I'm talking about get your things together to go out of town."

"Oh! I'm sorry. You scared me for a moment Daddy, I thought you meant something else." They all laughed and went to pack their things for the road.

Two hours later I received a phone call from Goldy Locs asking me have I left town yet? "Nah, Goldy I'm still here. Is there something you need?" I asked.

"Nah, I'm cool Mac Goldie. I just wanted to tell you that I heard from that fat bitch this morning. You was right Mac Goldie, that fat bitch was hiding out somewhere eating. She claims to be back home, and the reason she left was because I was starving her."

"The shit isn't funny, but damn Goldy Locs! A hotdog a day! What do you call that?" Goldy Locs tried to justify what he had done and said, "But Damn Pimping, the hoe acted as if she wanted me to help her lose weight."

"Yeah, lose weight not starve the bitch." I said this time more serious.

"You right Mac Goldie, maybe I should have let the bitch eat more than a damn hotdog!"

"But anyway, when are you leaving, and where are you headed?"

"I don't know where my destination is right now Goldy, but first I'm going to pull over in North Carolina and play them for two or three days. Then I'm going to skip over to Washington, D.C and break on them for about a day or two. Then go to Atlantic City and spend it all!"

"Damn Mac Goldie, I sure wish that I could go with you, but I know you been promising them girls some time with their Daddy on the road alone. I wish nothing but success on your journey Mac Goldie, stay in touch with me baby. You know I need to hear that spirit."

"For sure Goldy Locs, you do the same brother, and don't be sitting around with your head down waiting on that big bitch to come back, get your head back in the game baby, the Game need you and so do I."

After hanging up from Goldy, the girls were all in the car ready to leave. When I got inside the car, Infinity was playing one of my greatest hits by Curtis Mayfield, *Do be you and do be down.* I looked at my gas hand to see was it on Freddy or Eddie- Full or Empty. Just as I thought, my gas hand was already on "Freddy FULL" ready to hit the E-Way.

I let Jazz start off driving since I was a little tired from the strong weed that I smoked earlier. I was always able to ride shot gun and relax while one of the girls drive. I knew each one of my girls was legit with license, no warrants, knew how to drive safe and protect my life. This was part of the business. Anyone that worked for me must have their license or I.D and legit. I would never get on the highway with a stranger. Someone that doesn't know me, or I don't know them. A lot of Players have fell in the game because they were too quick to hit the highway with a stranger. They never took the time to know her real age, or could she stand up under pressure. Each one of my girls had been with me over three years. Out of them three years everyday was a test to see will you hold or fold.

Two and a half hours later we were close to North Carolina when we all noticed a big storm ahead of us.

"Damn Daddy! That looks like a tornado in front of us," Infinity said.

"Hoe cut that song off and put it on the weather station," I told Infinity. For sure we were heading into a bad storm. It was so bad until we couldn't go any further or turn around. I told Jazz to get off the highway and find a hotel so we could check in to a room.

"Daddy, there's a hotel," Melissa spotted sitting behind a bunch of rain. It was the Motel 6 and only had one room left with a single bed. The lady at the front desk didn't want to sell us the room because she couldn't believe how all of us was going to fit in that one bed? The girls convinced her by hugging one another saying, "Come on, we're all sisters, we grew up sleeping in the same bed."

The old white lady was impressed by their performance, then she said, "Well, where are you going to sleep young man?"

"Talking to me?" I said to the old lady. "Yes you," She said smiling. I peeped that she was flirting so I decided to flirt back and said, "Oh, I'm sleeping with you if you have another room." That statement was like a compliment to her, and it made her feel twenty years younger. The reason I say that is because she was ready to break the rules and give out a room she didn't have. "Here's a key for all of you guys, including the handsome young man," she continued to say smiling, "Don't have too much fun."

Once we got situated in the room, the girls and I wanted to play a game of Spades. Although, no one was able to work that night we still had fun. Building a foundation. When it was time for us to lay down, we all climbed in the same bed. Each one of the girls found their spot to lay close to me. From the outside looking in, any man would have love to be in the bed with four women, but on "The Inside of The Game," was nothing freaky about us. We were all family!

That next day, I was the first to open my eyes and seen that it was still raining. "GET UP GIRLS, we headed back to Atlanta. This storm is not going to let us go any farther." The look on the girls face was depressing. Especially Infiniti. I knew all the girls was ready to get out of Atlanta for a minute and spread their hoeing across the country, but no way we would have made it another mile going North. I called fly Ty to see was it raining in Atlanta, "What's happening Fly Ty?" "What's up kinfolks?" He spoke back. "Did you make it to North Carolina safe?" "Yeah mane! We here now, just ran into some bad weather."

"It rained all last night here too kinfolks, I had to bring the bitch in cause it was raining so bad."

"Bring her in for what! That bitch supposed to be inside them Mexicans house working, it wasn't raining in there." I knew Sara was having her way with Fly Ty and running circles around him. But this was part of the game that you have to figure out yourself with no one else help. I didn't tell Fly Ty that I was on my way back to Atlanta, I wanted to creep up on him to see what type of rest saving he was doing with Sara.

Chapter 26

The whole drive back home the girls were quiet as a mouse until I said, "You hoes can come out that depressed mode, and get back focused on what you need to be doing when we get back!"

When I pulled up to the apartment, I noticed someone was in my bedroom. Infinity noticed it too and said, "Daddy! I just seen someone look out your window!" *The girls didn't know that I had given Ty permission to stay at the house, but what the fuck was he doing in my room?* I told the girls to wait in the car while I checked to see who was in the house. When I opened the door, I immediately called Ty name, "FLY TY MANE WHERE THE FUCK YOU AT?" He wasn't in the front, so I knew as soon as I opened my bedroom door, he was going to be laid up in my bed with Sara. Sara opened the door before I could say anything saying, "Fly Ty is not here!"

"BITCH WHAT THE FUCK YOU DOIN IN MY ROOM? AND WHY YOUR ASS AIN'T AT WORK?" She turned her back towards me then said, "You're not my man anymore, I don't have to answer to you." Before I could kick her in the ass straight out my room, here comes Fly Ty, walking through the front door with a grocery bag talking about, "Damn kinfolks, when you get back?"

"FUCK THAT FLY TY! Mane what this bitch doing laying up in my bed, and why she not working?" Fly Ty tried his best to justify why she wasn't at work saying, "kinfolks it was raining so bad last night she got sick and that's why I told her to come in." Soon as he said something about her being sick Sara let out a counterfeit cough as if she had a cold.

Inside the grocery bag was all type of soup, oranges, juice and Ritz-Crackers. I grabbed the bag from Fly Ty and said, "Who is this for? Please don't say the **bitch**!" Before he could answer I cut him off and said, "Listen to me Fly Ty, the only thing is going to make a hoe feel well is when she get a bankroll for a Pimp. That's the best medication a hoe needs to get well."

"Dig that kinfolks! You right! Get your ass up bitch and get ready for work," Ty said. Not once did Sara hesitate or act as if she didn't want to go to work. She quickly grabbed her things and said to Fly Ty, "Do I have time take a shower?"

"Can she kinfolks?" Ty asked.

"Yeah, she can shower. I'm sure she knows where the shower is," I said. When Sara went pass me, she had a smirk on her face as if she knew what she was doing. Once she was in the shower, Fly Ty stepped to me trying to explain the Mis- Pimping he had done on Sara.

"Kinfolks, I know you think that I been bullshitting with this bitch, but I haven't." He continued to say while showing me the bankroll that Sara gave him, "You see kinfolks, I've been charging this bitch mane." He raised up a three-thousand-dollar trap that he got from Sara. I said to Fly Ty, "Dig this Fly, I'm not surprise to see the money you made off her, but what I do know is that you can make a lot more off that bitch if you put some Pimping in it."

"What you mean kinfolks? What you think I've been doing? I BEEN PIMPING ON THIS BITCH MANE!" I just looked at Fly Ty and didn't say nothing else about the Pimping. I knew that Sara was only getting him some "I Like You Money" because she did like him. One thing I know about this game is that a bitch can like you more than she love her favorite candy bar, but when a storm comes through to test the both of you to see will she hold up. If there's no Pimping in it, her feelings for you will blow away and so will she. It was a lot that Fly Ty had to learn about this game, and the only thing can teach him was "EXPERIENCE."
He had to learn not to put all of his belief into that one hoe. Because whenever she

did decide to leave him, she will take everything with her including his belief. "Dig this kinfolks, I'm going to catch a cab back over to Mexican Land and get me a room. Give me a few hours to lace this bitch up and put her back to work." "Do what you have to do Fly Ty, just be careful doing it."

The girls seen Fly Ty and Sara leaving the apartment and I'm sure they wanted to say something, but they knew not to get in a Pimp business. Later on that afternoon, I headed to Fly Ty room to scoop him up. He wanted me to take him to cop some weed, and he also wanted to treat a Pimp out for lunch. Soon as he got in the car, he started talking shit. "Yeah mane, I'm three-thousand dollars in front this bitch and I plan to have a thousand more before the day is over." I cut in while he was still popping game and said, "Don't burn your money Fly Ty!" Both of his eyebrows lifted up in curiosity and said, "What do you mean by that kinfolks?"

"What I mean is, don't count your money until it's in your hand."

"Damn you right kinfolks. I didn't think about it that way." Since Ty was still green to the "Pimp Life" I thought that I'll give him a little game to keep him from losing his freedom or worse than that, his life.

"Dig this Fly Ty, this isn't a game to trust too quick. What I mean is, you can't be too quick to put your trust in these hoes."

"Fly Ty cut in saying, "Oh no kinfolks! I know not to trust a hoe!"

"Just listen Fly Ty before you cut me off, it's cool to trust and believe in your hoe, but only when you see yourself inside of her. When a hoe starts to move the way you instructed her to, then you have you a hoe that you can say is all you. Trust or belief doesn't come overnight. It's a process. In the meantime, you need not to be where your hoe is working. Two plus two equals four, right? So, whenever they bust this bitch and your dumbass in the same room where she's working, who do you think going to jail?" He put both hands on top of his head at the same time and said, "BOTH OF US! DAMN KINFOLKS! It's a lot I have to learn about this game."

While Fly Ty and I was talking, I received a phone call from an unknown number. Usually, I wouldn't have answered it, but Fly Ty insisted that I should saying, "Answer it kinfolks! You never know it might be some money calling you."

"Hello," I said.

"Hey Daddy! This is Sara. I just hit a lick and I wanna come back home!"

"Where you at bitch?" I said in an unbelievable tone.

"The same apartments Daddy, will you please hurry and come get me? I'm scared that I'm not going to get away with this money, and I want to give it all to you so bad!"

"Chill Bitch!" I said. "Wait on me in that same McDonalds!" When I hung up the phone Fly Ty was doing the same thing he was doing when Sara call me wanting to give him some money, which was rolling a blunt.

"Who was that on the phone kinfolks?" I turned down the volume on the radio then said, "That was that Sara bitch."

"WHO?" Ty said while checking his pager and phone. This time I said it loud and clear, "YOU HEARD WHAT I SAID NIGGA, THAT WAS THAT SARA BITCH!" Still acting as if he didn't know what was about to happen Ty said, "I wonder why the bitch didn't hit my line. This damn phone must not be working or something!" I looked over at Ty and said, "It works kinfolks! That bitch just called my line talking about she wants to come back home, and that she just hit a lick." Immediately tears started to well up in Fly Ty's big hokey eyes when he said, "YALL GOT ME FUCKED UP! I DON'T PLAY LIKE THIS KINFOLKS!"

"PLAY LIKE WHAT FLY TY?" I asked. Then I continued to say, "This the same thing the bitch did to me three four nights ago, remember? I didn't start crying or say no square shit like you just said. I took it like a

PIMP and kept moving on. Same way you going to have to do Fly Ty!"

I seen the revenge in his eyes and was able to tell Sara was coming. He watched her every move until she was in the car. "Here you are Daddy!" She reached over my shoulder and handed me a twenty-two-hundred-dollar trap. "WOW!" is all I heard when I noticed Ty had jumped in the back seat continuing punching Sara in her ribs and face saying, "BITCH DON'T YOU EVER PLAY WITH ME NO MORE!!! FUNKY BITCH! LYING ASS HOE!" Bad as I wanted to tell him to chill, I couldn't. She had played a "Dangerous Game" with "The Game" and there was no way I can save her. Fly Ty was swinging out of emotions, and you can tell in every punch her threw.
"Save me some work Fly Ty," I spoke up and said. He spun his head all the way around and said, "say what cuz?"
"I said "SAVE ME SOME WORK! Meaning don't beat the bitch so bad that I can't work her." He finally climbed up off her

and jumped out the front seat, "YOU CAN
DROP ME OFF AT GREYHOUND
KINFOLKS, I'M NOT TRYING TO BE
AROUND THIS FAKE SHIT!"
"HOLD ON NOW FLY TY! AIN'T SHIT
FAKE ABOUT ME! I TOOK MY LICK IN
THE STOMACH THE SAME WAY YOU
GOT TO TAKE YOURS! YOU IN THE
WRONG GAME IF YOU CAN'T STAND TO
LOSE. NOW I'LL TAKE YOU TO
WHEREVER YOU WANT TO GO, BUT
YOU NEED TO KNOW NOT TO PUT TOO
MUCH TRUST IN A HOE OVERNIGHT!" Ty
stood outside the car just shaking his
head and swinging his arms back and
forth. I told Sara to sit up in the back seat.
"That shit you pulled bitch could have
cost you your life! Don't ever think that
you can play with someone emotions,
and don't expect shit like this to happen.
You know the reason why I couldn't get
involved right?"
"Yes Daddy," she said sniffing and crying
a little. I continued giving her some

understanding, "Well the good news is, all of this should be behind you now." She shook her head up and down without saying anything but was trying to say yes.

When Fly Ty got back into the car his spirit was better and conversation was different. Then he laughed out of nowhere and said to me, "Damn kinfolks! This game ain't for me!" I laughed back and said, "You right about that! You going to kill a hoe before you get any money out of her!" We both laughed and went back to being kinfolks. I took Sara to Ty room so she can get her things. She was still spook of what Ty would do to her until I said in front of Ty, "BITCH DIDN'T I TELL YOU TO MOVE FORWARD, THAT SHIT IS YOUR PAST!" She looked up at me still with fear in her eyes and said, "I know Daddy, I just feel real bad for doing what I did to you and Fly Ty."

"Don't feel bad now hoe, it's not like you got away with it. You took a mean ass whipping for what you did. Now it's time to put the past in our rearview and move forward, you understand?"

"Yes Daddy!" She replied.

The understanding that I gave Fly Ty about this part of the game help him with his pain and attitude. He had no problem with letting Sara get her things. How could a person be mad when you made three thousand dollars and some change in two days off a bitch? I watched him count the little money he had five times, as if he never had this much money before.

"Dig this Fly Ty, I'm about to take this bitch and get her a room, I also need to rap with her about a few things. Are you going to be okay until I get back? Or should I ask, are you going to be here when I get back?" Fly Ty stared at me like this was going to be his last time seeing me and said real low, "I'll be here." I can tell that he was still hurt about Sara and needed me there to hold him up. But this was part of the game that every great pimp must go through. You must know how it first feels to be on top of the world one day, then back all alone the next day. They call this part of the game "getting baptized." Once you've been baptized then receive the "Holy Spirit in The Game!" PIMPING IS AN ART! IT'S A GIFT TO BE BORN WITH!

Sara and I made it back on Buford Highway to get her a room, because there was no way I was going to bring her back to my apartment after what she had done. Just because I didn't break her jaw, or put my hands on her, didn't mean I wasn't going to make her feel it. I've learned in this game, over the years, that you don't always have to kick a hoe in the ass to make her feel you. All you have to do is take away what the hoe built to get close to you, for instance, her position, or give her a fine to pay for the violation, she committed against you. When you give a hoe a fine to pay, they usually don't pay it. They say, "fuck it" and then leave. Which is what you want anyway. At least you know that you didn't run out of Pimping to give the bitch, because every good Pimp knows when you run out of Pimping to give a bitch, then you become violent and start putting your hands on her.

This is an easy way to get yourself crossed out the game, and she knows this.

"Daddy, am I not able to come back around my sisters?" Sara asked.

"To be honest hoe, I don't think you ready to come around them. Not just because you don't deserve it, but because everyone in the family took what you did personal except me. It's all business with me until you make it personal. The girls look at you in a different way now, so it's best that you work by yourself, until you are able to be back around the girls." She dropped her head as if she have already gave up.

I was doing everything I could to blow her away and to never come back. I left her all alone in the room by herself so that she could think about the bad choices she made. I really thought that Sara and I was going to have a good start and a long ending. But right when you count one of these hoes in too quick without letting her go through the process "The Game" will show you every time that she wasn't for you. I wasn't going to miss her. She didn't stay long enough for me to feel anything. *DAMN! I'm already take it as if she's gone.*

I learned to prepare myself for whenever I sent one of the girls out the door to work, that it wasn't a guarantee she will be back. This helps me not to act emotional whenever a hoe does leave. Now if I would have believed in everything she said when she told me, "DADDY, I promise to never leave you." Then when she does decide to leave and not come back there you are feeling like a sucker! They say in the Game, you must have the understanding that every hoe has an expiration date. They come to pay not stay, then be on their way to the next player to do the same thing.

Once I finished from dropping Sara off I headed back to check on Fly Ty to see was he still at his room. Just as I thought, he had checked out his room and went back to Memphis. I knew Fly Ty wasn't going to be able to stand on his two feet from a lick that knocked him down. He was too embarrassed to see Sara was back with me, and that he was back whoreless. I understood the escape he made. At least he didn't go back home broke! He had three thousand dollars in cash, and a good story on how he got the money. I had a feeling inside of me that Sara will be gone too when I get back to the room. Before I could get out the car, I noticed that the curtains in her room was pulled back with no luggage or sight of Sara inside. I shook my head back and forth *Maybe the bitch and Fly Ty have got back together.* It wouldn't have surprised me. After Sara saw that things wasn't the same when she came back, it was too unbearable for her to deal with.

I rode back to the apartment thinking to myself something that a Great Pimp said to me, He said, "When you try and teach a sucker the game that's not a Pimp, he will turn the game around and treat you like the sucker." Then I thought again to myself, *Fly Ty is far from being a sucker, he just wasn't a Pimp, and didn't know how to control his feelings.*

As I was thinking, I received a phone call from a private number.
"HELLO," I said. "HELLO!" No one said anything so I hung up the phone. I figured it was Sara missing me already. Usually when you give a hoe some good game then she leaves you, they always call back for some more game or just hold the phone ashamed to say who they are. Again, the phone rung, but this time I didn't answer. I knew it was Sara, and I wasn't about to play hide and go seek with her over the phone. If she wanted to talk with me, she knew what it took. Hoes talk with their bankroll not with a bunch of sorries and stories.

When I pulled up to the apartment the girls were outside playing "Double Dutch." Look at this Shit!! You would have thought these hoes was best friends or real sisters the way they were laughing and having fun. Soon as I got out the car Infinity said, "Come on Daddy, let's see can you jump rope." I attempted to put my leg out as if I was going to start jumping, then I stopped the rope with my hand and said, "Double Dutch is for girls baby, it's not a Pimp sport. But I will let you ladies continue to play 10 years old for a little while longer, then you all need to come inside and get ready like Hoes and go to work."

"Yes Daddy!" They all said, then start back to jump roping. They made the game look so fun until the little girls from the neighborhood came over wanting to play. Look what you hoes done started! A damn double Dutch tournament.

I would like to say this to all inquiring minds that want to know whether or not a Pimp allowed his hoes to have this type of fun? Although, we work 365 days out of a year, it's healthy for you to let your girls still feel human. Just because you have raise them to be serious, fast and

cold-hearted hoes, doesn't mean she
don't want to act like a child every now
and then.

Chapter 27

I went upstairs to roll myself a blunt when I received a phone call from an old friend that I knew since I been here in Atlanta.

"HELLO," I answered. "What's happening Mac Goldie The Game?" A voice said on the other end of the phone. It was Scooter. A True-Blue Ribbon Friend!!

"What's Up with you Scooter?" I said happy to hear from him!

"Ain't too much shaking Goldie, just trying to see were you still here in Atlanta? Or what state are you in?"

"Yeah, I'm still here bro, what you need? Is everything okay?"

"Not really Mac Goldie. I need some cash real fast!"

"DAMN BRO! That type of fast cash gets you in a shit load of trouble. How much do you need?" I asked out of concern. He laughed then said, "I need at least twenty-five thousand, but I know you not trying to give me that. So, I need your help with setting off this Jewelry Heist."

"WHAT! DAMN BRO! You know I haven't did no shit like that in years. I've been Pimping for over ten years now. All I been doing is dressing, resting and finessing the game. Now you asking me to be a Gorilla again?"

He laughed again, then said, "I'm serious Goldie!! I need you bro!! All I need you to do is help me get a stolen car and have one of your girls drive it to a cool spot. If you do that bro, I'll give you a Rolex and five thousand dollars." He knew what to say to make the antennas come out my head. The offer he was giving was tempting.

"Still," I said, "I need some time Big Bro to think about this one."

"HOW LONG?" he asked? "Because I'm trying to do this before this weekend."

"Give me today to think it over. I'll call you later this evening with my decision." In his voice, I can hear the sincereness when he said, "Goldie Please! I need you Bro!"

I really had to think about this one. I didn't want to make a decision that will end my career or take my freedom. The way Scooter was sounding so thirsty really made me feel uncomfortable. He acted as if there was no time left to do it, almost like the world was going to blow up in five minutes.

Scooter was a good friend of mines that I met when I first came to Atlanta. I met his Mother before I met him, Miss Charlene was her name. She was the manager at these apartments where she rented me a studio. I remembered her asking me, "Goldie you hungry? All I ever see you eat is a bunch of junk food. Why don't you let me cook you a hot plate? "Yes Ma'am," I said. She asked me, "Do you like Cubed steak and rice, with some Jiffy cornbread and string beans?" I looked at Miss Charlene like she was speaking Spanish, because I never had cubed steak before. Especially, with rice.

The only thing that I ate rice with was bacon, sausage and toast, with sugar on it. Five minutes later dinner was ready. I thought that I was going to sneak off and eat the plate in my room, but she invited me to come in her apartment and sit down at a real table to eat.

Inside her apartment were three more kids that was hers. Tasha, Head and Yoke. They all were younger than me. "Okay, dinner is ready," Miss Charlene said. "Make sure you all wash your hands before you come to this table." They all made me feel like I was part of the family.

After blessing our food no one said anything else until we was finished. I never had a meal so damn good! She didn't have to wash my plate; I licked my plate all clean and asked her could I have seconds. "Sure, you can," Miss Charlene said. "As a matter of fact, you can take a plate for later."
"Thank you, Miss Charlene. I really do appreciate you for helping me since I been here." She waved her hands and said to

me, "Boy, you don't have to thank me for no food! What I would like for you to do is meet my oldest son. His name "Scooter." He can you use someone like you to hang around and learn a few things."
"How old is he Miss Charlene," I asked?
"He's 18 years old about to be 19 in a few months." I was 20 years old at the time, so I guess by me being a couple of years older than Scooter she felt I could teach him something.

I still can remember when him and I first met. He pulled up in an old school 1988 "Nighty Eight Buick" With some Reverse Eight Rims on it. The paint color looked electric blue. Mane he looked so cool to hang out with! At the time I was wanted for a murder charge in Memphis, Tennessee. So, I wasn't trying to hang out with anyone that could get me caught up. He jumped out bumping this song by Goodie Mob called *RED DOGS.*
"What's up Goldie?" He surprised me when he knew my name, so I surprised him back and said, "What's happening

Scooter?" He laughed then asked, "How you know my name? My mama must've told you?" I said, "Yep, same way she told you my name." We gave one another dap then Scooter said, "My Mama told me a lot about you. She said all you do is hang around these apartments and don't go anywhere." He threw me the keys to his car and said, "You know your way around Atlanta?" I'm standing there stuck don't know what to say, "Um, what do you want me to do with these keys?"

"Drive Nigga! You do know how to drive, don't you?"

"Yeah, I know how to drive but I don't have any license. Plus, I'm cool. I can't afford to go out." He insisted that I go out with him and said, "Don't worry about no money! I got you."

It was another dude that rode with us name Tony. He was from Miami. Looked like he could have played for the Miami Dolphin's by his weight and height. He wouldn't have killed a Mosquito if it bit him twice, big soft ass nigga. We went inside this club called "Shirley Show Case." It was located on the East Side of Town. With me not being from Atlanta, I wasn't hip to the uniform the police officers wore.

There was this tall white guy following me around the club, so I caught him in the bathroom and said, "Listen bitch ass white boy! You need to stop motherfucking following me!" I really thought that he was the security for the club. On our way out the club headed back to the car, he came out of nowhere yelling, "GET THE FUCK DOWN AND PUT YOUR HANDS BEHIND YOUR BACK! It was the same white boy that I roasted inside of the club. With him was Dekalb County Police Department! *SHIT! I'm fucking through,* I said to myself.

Inside of Scooter car was three loaded handguns. A 9mm, A .380 and A 12 Gage Shotgun. I felt like I was about to throw up I was so sick. The Officer that I went off on inside the club opened the door and said, "Hey You! Tough ass! Get your ass out the car NOW!" He let me know what I said to him offended him by saying, "You still don't want me following you? Now listen to me you little black fucker, which one of them guns are yours?"

"What Guns?" I played stupid.

"Okay, you little bastard! We'll see once I check for fingerprints. Now get your ass back in the car!" He pulled Big Tony out next. Scooter had already told Tony he would take two of the gun charges if Tony would only claim the .380. Like I said earlier, Tony was a Pussy! Trapped in a Man's body.

The Officer opened up the door again and said, "Okay, since neither one you thugs want to say who this other gun belongs to, I'll just charge each one of you with each gun. Three bodies, three guns." We all went to Dekalb County Jail for "Carrying A Concealed Weapon." I had given up once we got fingerprinted. Although, I only had a $250 bond I just knew they was going to call me back to book in for the Murder charge I was facing in Memphis.

Scooter woke me from my bad dream and said, "Why you still laying down when you need to be trying to make bond before they catch up with you? Call my Pop's Mr. C, to come sign your bond." I couldn't believe that Scooter was already trying to take all the gun charges for me, now he's trying to get me out before himself. *DAMN, I said to myself, UNBELIEVABLE.* Three hours later they was calling my name to go home. I gave Scooter a real appreciation hug and said, "Whatever you need me to do for you, I GOT YOU!" I didn't know that I wasn't going to see him until 7 months later. They gave him two years for the gun charges. Even when he came home over the years, he still had my back. Now twelve years later, here he is asking me for a favor. You see why it's hard for me to tell him no because of what he has done for me. All that night I thought about what could happen to me and my career. I could lose everything I worked for including my freedom I was still willing to help him this last time.

Chapter 28

I gave him a call the next morning, "What's up Nigga? You still ready to pull this off? I could feel him smiling through the phone as he said, "You damn right I'm ready! So, what you saying, you all in?" "Count me in brother, I can't let you do this by yourself. But after this, I'm done." Scooter had already got his crew together and was waiting on me so we can hit the road. I brought only Jazz with me and she was unaware of what we were doing. It's best that she knew nothing, so whenever anyone ask her anything about what's happening she honestly knew nothing to tell them.

Scooter rode with Jazz and me while the crew followed us to the next state. Breaking the silence in the car Scooter said, "Goldie remember that time you and my cousin Jr got into it?"
"Yeah, I remember. I remember having to beat that nigga ass for trying to gorilla my shit!" Scooter laughed until he was crying

273

with tears as he continued telling the story, "Man I still can remember the way you snatch that shirt over his head so that he couldn't see anything, then you went to work on his ass. Can you believe after him trying to take your shit and you getting on his ass, this nigga had the nerve to ask me to help him? That shit was unbelievable." Yeah, Scooter mane we done had some wild times together." All the stories we told from the past had Jazz in shock of who she was in the car with.

"Dig this Scooter, I'm going to have Jazz get a room in another city for us. Once you park the car Jazz, then I want you to come back and get me."

"From where?" Jazz asked.

"The room Bitch!"

"I'm sorry Daddy! I didn't know where I was supposed to come get you, I don't even know what's going on!"

"That's a good thing Bitch," I said. "Don't asked no questions so you won't be able to give any answers."

"Okay Daddy," Jazz said.

Once we all made it to our destination, Scooter and I went separate ways so that he can get his crew together. While Jazz and I was alone she tightly grabbed my hand and said, "Daddy, I don't mean to sound like I'm getting into your business, but may I asked you something?"

"Sure, Baby girl! What's on your mind?" She hesitated before saying anything then said, "Are you sure you're not going to get mad?"

"I am now Bitch! If you don't spit out what you have to say!"

"Okay Daddy, I just want to know what's going on? Because whatever it is, you seem frustrated and not for sure if you want to do it. Before you go off on me Daddy, just remember, you the one who told me, that if you ever feel uncomfortable about something you doing, DON'T DO IT!" As bad as I wanted to slap Jazz in the mouth for telling the truth, I couldn't. She was exactly right about everything. She had peeped game that I was uncomfortable about what I was doing. And I was taking out my frustration on her.

"Dig this Jazz, you're right about what you said, but baby girl it's not that serious as you think. All I need for you to do is drive the car to a certain spot and leave it. Then you can drive back to Atlanta and wait to hear from me." I can feel the look in her eyes that she was also uncomfortable about driving the car. But I wasn't trying to go into details with Jazz about the lick we was getting ready to do.

That next day Jazz was up before me thinking which wasn't a good think. "What's up baby girl? Is everything cool?" I asked Jazz.

"Yes Daddy, it's just I couldn't sleep the whole night thinking what's about to happen? You don't have to tell me, but at least let me ride back with you so that I know you safe with me."

"Okay my Baby Angel, I'll let you protect me on this trip back home. Just promise me not to worry so much okay?"

"I promise Daddy," she said as she pulled her body close to mines for a hug. I didn't go with Scooter and his crew on the lick. I've done what he wanted me to do, which was provide the transportation to the right location. All I was doing now is waiting for the good news. It's been going on thirty minutes and still no call from Scooter. Right when I was about to call my phone rung, it was Scooter.

"Hello, Bro where you at?" Scooter said sounding excited!!

"Me and Jazz still at the room waiting on you. What's up with you? Is everything cool?" He screamed through the phone, "YOU DAMN RIGHT ITS COOL, WE GOOD! Meet me at that exit that I told you to scoop me."

"DIG THAT!" I said! I knew from the tone of his voice and the sound of his spirit that the lick had went through.

It took me less than ten minutes to make it to the exit where Scooter was. There he was. With two big bags filled with jewelry. He jumped in the back seat then said, "Turn that song up!" It was a song on the radio by Trick Daddy called *Dade County.* He emptied out the bag and there it was! Nothing but pretty ass Rolex watches!

"OH MY GOD!" Jazz said. Her mouth was wide open, and her eyes were about to pop out of her head. She never seen them many Rolex watches all brand new. "WE RICH BABY!" IS WHAT SCOOTER SAID.

We all was so excited and bouncing around inside of the car until we didn't notice a State Trooper was parked ahead clocking. Scooter and I ducked down real quick so that he couldn't see nobody but Jazz driving. Lucky for us, Jazz was white and doing the speed limit. This is the reason we needed Jazz to drive. Her skin will always make it through before ours. "Daddy, he didn't come out?" Jazz said. Now all we needed was for Scooter crew to pass him. YES! The Game was on our side. They slid pass him the same way we did. It was two more hours before we made it back to Atlanta safe and successful.

"Hey Goldie, what do you think about me selling a couple of watches to Mr. Rainwater?" Scooter asked?

"Who you say?" I said back not believing what he asked me. "Didn't he say the Feds been watching him? I don't think that's a good ideal Scoot."

"Well Goldie Man, I need to dump at least two watches so that I can get out this hole I'm in. Do you have twenty thousand to give me until I sell some of these watches?"

"Hell Nah, Nigga!! I think you do need to call Rainwater's." We both laughed as Scooter picked up his phone to call him. "Whatever you do Scooter, don't tell him you around me!"

Chapter 29

Mr. Rainwater was a bogus ass white guy that Scooter done business with before. He was a greedy pig that never had enough to eat. He would come to Atlanta just to round up a couple of guys to do crimes for him. Also, I had done business with him by setting up a few girls to date a couple of Sheriffs in his county. Like I said, Rainwater was bogus, and so was the Judges and Sheriffs.

Scooter got off the phone with Mr. Rainwater and said, "He want all the watches." They agreed to meet on Fulton Industrial at a room once we checked in. "Damn Scoot! You told him you had more than two watches? Mane, I don't trust that cracker at all!"

"Me either Scooter said. He's the only one I can get 20 thousand from." Something just didn't seem right.

On the side of the road, we saw over fifteen State Trooper cars, all the way to Fulton Industrial.

Once we checked in the Best Western Hotel on Fulton Industrial, Scooter gave Mr. Rainwater a call. It seemed as if he had been waiting on our call all day the way he answered the phone on the first ring.

"Hello Scooter, is this you?"

"Yeah man this me!"

"Why you sounding so paranoid?" Scooter asked Rainwater.

"I'm not paranoid, I just can't wait to get my hands on them watches! What's your room number?" Rainwater's said quickly. Scooter wasn't stupid or slow to give up the room number, so he said, "I'm not at the room yet, I'm sending Jarvis and Trey to sell you two of the watches. I'll bring you the rest of them later."Rainwater hesitated for a moment then said, "I sure wish you would have gave them more than two to sell me, because I brought a friend who wanted to buy them all.

"Okay cool, just tell your friend I will have the rest of the watches for him later," Scooter said. When he hung up the phone, Scooter was looking like he didn't trust what Rainwater was saying on the other end. I read his mind and said, "What did Rainwater say on the phone Scooter that got you looking different?" He played it off and said, "Nah, everything straight. He just was asking about the rest of the watches, talking about, he has someone with him that wants to buy them all." I didn't trust Rainwater at all! And Scooter knew it.

"Why don't we go downstairs and see what's taking the guys so long?" Scooter said to change subjects.

"Good idea, I said. I was starting to feel a little uncomfortable sitting in this room anyways. "Wait for us to come back Jazz. Keep your eyes on these watches," I instructed her.

"Yes Daddy," She said, still in awe staring at all the watches without looking up.

Looking at the numbers on the elevator go down from the 10th floor to the lobby. Soon as the elevator opened up, there was over fifty officers rushing us coming towards the elevator.

"CLOSE THE ELEVATOR SCOOT!" I yelled. Lucky for us the elevator closed before their reaching arms could grab us. As the elevator was going up you can hear them yelling, "ITS GOING TO THE 4TH FLOOR, NO 5TH FLOOR, 6TH FLOOR as their voices faded away. When the door opened up on the 10th floor, we both ran toward the room to get Jazz and the watches.

"COME ON BITCH!" I said as grabbed the watches and passed them to Scooter. "Hey bro, let's split up" I said. I'll meet back up with you if you get away."

Scooter took the stairways as me and Jazz stayed on the 10th floor. Soon as he made it to the last floor you can hear the officers screaming, "THERE HE IS, THERE HE IS! GET HIM!"

I stuck my head from the balcony in the room and seen them all chasing him. *This was my break.*

"Jazz, here's the keys to the car. Go downstairs and pop the trunk and call and tell me when it's cool to jump." I reached inside my pocket and gave her the two Rolexes Scooter promised us. Before she left, I grabbed her by her head and kissed her forehead as if I never was going to see her again.

"Daddy I'm scared!" I can feel Jazz's body shaking.

"It's okay baby, you can do this! Just call and let me know when I can come." She stayed on the phone with me the whole time she got into the car.

"Daddy! Daddy! I'm passing them all now. I seen two of the guys that was with Scooter in the back of the police car."

"DID THEY SEE YOU?" I asked before she could say another word.

"I think so, but no one is paying attention to me. They all are in a huddle talking."

"Okay, pop the trunk like I said baby."

"I already have Daddy, Where you at?"

"I'm coming down to a lower floor Jazz so that I can jump from there and get in the trunk."

There I was on the second floor. The car and Jazz waiting on me. At first, I had

doubt, *what if they see me soon as I land on the ground? What if they pull the car over before we make it out the parking lot?* **I'm thinking too much with only a little time to do what I have to do. Here I Go! "BOOM!" I landed and scared the shit out of Jazz when I jumped in the trunk. Once I was in the trunk, I pulled out the seat from the back to talk with Jazz.**

"Where are they Hoe?" I asked praying that we get away.

"They all still standing in the middle right here where I'm about to pass. Daddy, one of the officers are telling me to go a different way because they have this exit blocked off."

"Is he telling you to stop, because you better not stop hoe!"

"No Daddy calm down you starting to spook me! We are away from them now; you can come out the trunk." As soon as I was climbing out the trunk to the back seat, there was still over 20 State Trooper cars parked on the side of the expressway.

"Damn Hoe! Are they coming out?"
"No Daddy, just stay back there until the road is clear."

They had over a hundred police cars looking for us and a helicopter circling around the area. I didn't know if Scooter was caught or not. I told Jazz to keep going 75 NORTH until we make it to another state. Finally, we made it out the state of Georgia! I took the phone I was using to talk with Scooter and tossed it out as we were driving. I couldn't believe that I had made a wrong decision that could cost me my freedom. My hoe Jazz was confused. She didn't know why I would involve myself into something that could end my career. But she didn't say anything. We just kept driving all the way to Indiana, Indianapolis, where Jazz and I first met. The rest of the girls didn't have a clue of what was going on. They had no way of contacting me other than call through Jazz phone. And I wasn't sure if anyone knew her number by heart. DAMN! This was too much to embrace. One wrong move done caused a major setback. Right when I didn't think my situation could get any worse it did!

Chapter 30

Jazz received a collect phone call from Pre-Trial County Jail saying it was Infinity. To accept charges, please press 5 or press 0 and hang.

"What do you want me to do Daddy?" Jazz asked.

"Go head and accept it hoe," I told Jazz.

"HELLO! HELLO! Can you hear me Jazz?"

"Yeah, I hear you, what's up?" Sounding frustrated through the phone Infinity said, "you see what's up! Me and Michelle is locked up. Have you heard from Daddy?" Before Jazz could lie I cut in saying, "I'm right here baby. Don't say nothing over the phone just wait to hear from a lawyer or a bond." Infinity acted as if she didn't hear anything I said and said, "DADDY WE DON'T HAVE NO BOND!! THEY TALKING ABOUT YOU IN ALOT OF TROUBLE AND THAT THE FEDS ARE LOOKING FOR YOU. IS THAT TRUE DADDY?"

"BITCH LIKE SAID, STAY QUIET AND WAIT TO HEAR FROM A LAWYER! Hang up the phone Jazz! That bitch is going to get everybody caught up!" Jazz was starting to sound worried, "Daddy you think the Feds are looking for us?" I told her the truth.

"I Don't know Baby girl. Just when the time do comes don't say anything to nobody until I get us all a lawyer."

"Yes Daddy," Jazz said with the little belief she was still trying to have in me.

Once we made it to the Nap town, Indiana, Indianapolis, Jazz and I went to an old friend of mines and stayed a night. Her name was Nikki. I was living with her before I met Jazz, but it didn't work out with us. She didn't want to sell any Pussy.

Nicki could tell something was troubling me, by the way I kept peeping out the window.

"Are you okay Goldie," she asked?

"Yeah, I'm cool Nicki, I just got a lot of shit on my mind."

"Well, I'm going to bed, there's a comforter in the closet if you or Jazz need it. Goodnight."

"Goodnight Nikki," Jazz and I said. "And thanks again for letting us stay here tonight."

I couldn't sleep at all last night, so I was the first to be up.

"Good morning Daddy, did you get any rest?" I lied and said, "Yeah I slept for a few hours. Do you want to ride with me and go scoop up Trina boyfriend? I promised that I would work out with him this morning and plus teach his son how to drive." I still can remember. It was 7:10am. The birds were singing to one another when I went outside. A beautiful day to be free. When I pulled up to get Roney and his son, I noticed a Sheriff's car was posted in front of the apartments. I wasn't scared or anything because I knew the car wasn't hot, and no way they could have known what happened in Georgia.

Once Roney and Mark got in the car Roney said, "Be careful. They've been pulling people over early this morning." Soon as we pulled out the apartments, here he comes flashing his disco lights. I kind of felt like something was about to go bad so I took off my Rolex and gave it to Jazz.

"Dig this Jazz, if anything happens to me, call Mrs. Rockwell and have her check on me."

"Is everything okay Goldie?" Roney asked. Before I could answer him, the police was already saying on the loud speaker, "Driver, step out of the car!" I noticed once I had stepped out there were three to four more police cars pulling up. "Get down on both of your knees and put your hands on top of your head!" Immediately, two undercovers came out of nowhere, kicked me in my back, causing me to land flat on my stomach and then said, "take them stolen earrings out of his ear and where is the rest of the jewelry you fucking thief!"

They ran everybody name in the car and only put me in handcuffs. They said that I was wanted out of Georgia for "Conspiracy to Commit Robbery." All I could do is drop my head and ask God to have mercy on my Pimping. Although, this had nothing to do with Pimping and Hoeing, Jazz still was believing in me and wanted me to let her know what to do. My mind wasn't working therefore I had no game to give her. I can still remember her breaking down crying and asking me, "Daddy, what you want me to do?" The officers were real assholes. They told Jazz, "Get your ass back, and don't say nothing to him!" They scoop me up from off the ground then threw me in the Patty Wagon. Once I made it to Marion County Jail, I was placed in segregation waiting to see some detectives. I sat there waiting for at least eight hours to find out what was going on. Suddenly, the door opened.

"JONES, WAKE UP! There's some detectives from Georgia who wants to talk to you.

Inside an interrogation room, was two white men looking like the Grand Wizard and one of his Klan.

"Hello, Mr. Goldie," one of the white guys said addressing me by my "Game Name." My name is Detective Sweat and this my Sergeant. I looked at them both up and down then said, "Okay, but what does knowing you have to do with me?"

"A lot," he answered. "Do you know Rainwater?"

"No, I Don't!" I answered.

Then the other white guy who was supposed to be the Sergeant said, "Listen Goldie, we really don't want you. The Feds want you more than we do, so you have bigger problems than this. If you don't tell me about Mr. Rainwater and your best friend Scooter, I'm going to make sure all three of you get the maximum sentence on this case." They was trying to squeeze me, and I knew it. So, I said, "I have nothing to talk about. I'm just ready to wave my rights to be extradited back to..."

"Excuse me, what's the name of your county jail?"

"DOUGLASVILLE!" The detective screamed in my ear real loud! I showed no weakness to his frustration or the way he was trying to intimidate me then I said to him, "Well, I'm ready for you guys to take me to Georgia so that I can get a bond." They both burst out laughing at the same time. Then, the Wizard said, "I GUARANTEE YOU, A BOND YOU WILL NOT GET IN DOUGLASVILLE COUNTY!"

"DAMN!" I said. "Is it that racist in your county?" He didn't answer but gave me a look that said, YOU'RE DAMN RIGHT WE'RE RACIST! Then I said something that I thought would make them feel like their county wasn't more powerful than God and I said, "Well Detectives, just in case you two done forgot, there is a GOD and that's who I have on my side."

"GOD?" The Grand Wizard looking Detective scooted his chair close to mines and looked at me with them reptile eyes then said, "YOU KNOW WHAT GOLDIE? I BELIEVE IN GOD TOO, BUT EVEN HE CAN'T GET YOU OUT OF THIS ONE. SEE YOU IN GEORGIA!"

............TO
BE CONTINUE.

Made in the USA
Columbia, SC
31 July 2024

39239921R00163